PRANA

PRANA

The Secret of Yogic Healing

Atreya

SAMUEL WEISER, INC.

York Beach, Maine

First published in 1996 by
Samuel Weiser, Inc.
P.O. Box 612
York Beach, ME 03910-0612

Library of Congress Cataloging-in-Publication Data
Atreya.
    Prana : the secret of Yogic healing / Atreya.
        p.   cm.
    Includes bibliographical references and index.
    (pbk. : alk. paper)
    1. Prânayâma — Therapeutic use. I. Title.
  RM727.Y64A87 1996
    615.5'3 — dc20   96-15586
                                                        CIP

ISBN 0-87728-885-2
BJ

Typeset in Stone Serif and Boffo

Illustrations copyright © 1996 Atreya

Cover illustration "Enlightenment" Copyright © 1996 Pichai
Nirand. Used by permission. Visual Dhamma Gallery, Thailand.

Printed in the United States of America

04 03 02 01 00 99 98 97 96
10 9 8 7 6 5 4 3 2 1

The paper used in this publication meets the minimum require-
ments of the American National Standard for Permanence of
Paper for Printed Library Materials Z39.48–1984

TO SRI H.W.L. POONJAJI

Self is what you are. You are That
Fathomlessness in which experience
  and concepts appear.
Self is the Moment which
  has no coming or going.
It is the Heart, Atman, Emptiness.
It shines to Itself, by Itself, in Itself.
Self is what gives breath to life,
You need not search for It, IT IS HERE.
You are That through which you would search.
You *are* what you are looking for!
And That is All it is.
Only Self is.

—H.W.L. Poonja
The Truth Is

TABLE OF CONTENTS

LIST OF FIGURES

LIST OF TABLES

ACKNOWLEDGMENTS

The following sources have been used for the quoted material at the chapter openings of this book: *Astavakra Samhita,* translated by Swami Nityaswarupananda (Calcutta: Advaita Ashrama, 1990), p. 194 (147); *The Caraka Samhita,* translated by Dr. Ram Sharma and Dr. Bhagawan Dash (Varanasi, India: Chowkhamba Sanskrit Series, 1992), xxv.33 (127); *The Eight Upanisads,* translated by Swami Gambhirananda (Calcutta: Advaita Ashrama, 1992), vol. I, pp. 204-205 (32), p. 201 (37), vol. II, p. 439 (xix), p. 436 (20); Dattatreya Avadhuta, *Avadhuta Gita,* translated by Swami Chetanananda (Calcutta: Advaita Ashrama, 1988), p. 76 (119), p. 97 (140); Paul Brunton, *Conscious Immortality: Conversations with Ramana Maharshi* (Tiruvannamalai, India: Sri Ramanashramam, 1984), p. 25 (53); Sri Nisargadatta Maharaj, *Consciousness and the Absolute,* edited by Jean Dunn (Durham: Acorn Press, 1994), p. 11 (1), p. 31 (13); Sri Nisargadatta Maharaj, *Prior to Consciousness,* edited by Jean Dunn (Durham: Acorn Press, 1985), p. 33 (55), p. 63 (80), p. 64 (98) p. 35 (110); Kavyakanta Ganapathi Muni, *Sri Ramana Gita* (Tiruvannamalai, India: Sri Ramanashramam, 1992) p. 51, v. 77 (7); Sri Sankaracarya, *Vivekacudamani,* translated by Swami Madhavananda (Calcutta: Advaita Ashrama, 1992), p. 31 (25); Sir John Woodroffe, *The Serpent Power* (Madras: Ganesh & Co., 14th ed., 1989), p. 74 quoting The Kaušitaki Upanisad 3.2 (16).

ACKNOWLEDGMENTS

FOREWORD

Prana is the life-force that vitalizes everything in the universe. Ultimately, it is the energy of consciousness itself, responsible for all movement in this conscious world. All systems of medicine work through some aspect of prana, even if they do not understand what it is. While allopathic medicine does not recognize prana as an entity in itself, prana still affects our vitality in various ways, which allopathic medicine may describe as circulation or homeostasis. Therefore, one could say that all healing is pranic healing.

Naturalistic systems of medicine are based upon an understanding of the life-force and how to keep it in balance. Prana itself, which is a Sanskrit word meaning vital force, is the basis of Ayurveda, the traditional natural healing system of India. Ayurveda means the science *(veda)* of life *(ayur)*. Ayur, life, itself is a synonym for prana. Ayurveda is a pranic medicine and all its therapies are based upon a recognition of the life-force and the various means to balance it.

Pranic healing also relates to the system of Yoga. Yoga is not just a system of exercise, or even of meditation. It is a way of working with the subtle energies of body and mind, the foremost of which is prana. The yogic science of Pranayama and its various breathing exercises are based upon understanding prana and how to work with it. Without a development of prana, we cannot go far on any yogic path. We will simply lack the vitality to pursue it.

Natural systems of medicine use various substances as vehicles for prana, such as food or herbs. These are defined energetically according to their heating and cooling attributes, or their elements and qualities; that is, according to how they affect our prana. Both Ayurveda and Chinese medicine have these systems of classifications. All the different diets and herbs prescribed are done to affect the vital force in a specific manner.

When we visit doctors or healers it is not *what* they pre-scribe for us alone that helps us. We first of all respond to the healing force, the prana or vitality, of the practitioners. We may feel this in how they speak to us or how they take our pulse. We come into their aura of healing, the field of their prana. If the therapist is warm, friendly, confident, and compassionate (that is, vibrant with prana), we respond positively to them and fol-low their recommendations happily. Without some pranic rap-port with the therapist, treatment is not likely to have a good result.

Natural medical systems also employ various actions that work on prana, such as acupuncture, bodywork, or Pancha Karma (Ayurvedic purification practices). In these cases, they are treating prana more directly. Touch, itself, in any form, com-municates prana because touch is the sensory quality that re-lates to the air element, with which prana or breath is connected.

It is possible, moreover, to use prana directly for healing purposes, whether together with other vehicles for prana, like food or herbs, or by itself. We can learn to project the power of prana directly to heal ourselves or others. Various direct ways of working with prana exist, such as pranayama (breathing ex-ercises). We can project the energy of the breath directly, using the power of the mind, particularly through visualization. Wherever we place our attention, we are also placing some as-pect of our prana or vitality. The more powerful our concentra-tion, the greater the power of prana we can impart. Bodyworkers know the importance of regulating their breathing, along with treating the patient; this ensures a more positive flow of heal-ing energy. Acupuncturists and acupressurists know the impor-tance of putting their chi into the acupuncture points.

Using prana directly for healing purposes, however, is not always easy. It requires first cultivating one's own prana, which in turn requires various disciplines: physical, mental, and spiri-tual. To directly influence the life-force of another, we must be certain that our own life-force and our motivations are pure. Our goal should be to serve as a vehicle for the cosmic prana, not to gain some power or glorify ourselves as healers, and cer-tainly not to interfere with the patient's natural flow of vital energy according to our own concepts or desires.

Ayurveda recommends a vegetarian diet for those who wish to be pranic healers. If we take meat, we are taking in the energy of death which will interfere with our own life-force. We should also practice *ahimsa*, or non-violence, because any form of violence makes our life-force negative.

All diseases, whether physical or mental, reflect some breakdown of pranic energy. The result is debility, depression, and disturbed emotions, all of which indicate pranic imbalances. For this reason, any disease can be treated through prana. Those who can impart a pure prana to their patients need not worry about the details of diagnosis. By imparting a pranic force, they can go directly to the heart of all our health problems.

There is a new pranic healing movement in India today that is connecting to similar therapies throughout the world as part of the new renaissance in natural medicine. However, up to now it has been very difficult to find books, or even authentic material on pranic healing, in the West.

Atreya, in his book *Prana: The Secret of Yogic Healing*, introduces this science and fills this need. He examines the nature of prana and its functions in the physical body, subtle body, and mind, including its relationship with the chakras. Notably, he gives various practical exercises for developing our own prana and for treating others with it. His book is filled with information and imparted with enthusiasm, reflecting the deep cultivation of his own prana. The book serves not only as an excellent introduction into pranic healing, but can also be used as a manual on the subject. It is useful for both the lay reader and for therapists.

Atreya introduces pranic healing in a spiritual context and connects it with deeper Vedantic teachings aiming at Self-realization. In this way, he directs the reader through pranic healing to Self-knowledge. The spiritual orientation of the book enhances its quality and brings the reader to a deeper level of self-understanding.

—Dr. David Frawley
author of *Ayurvedic Healing, Tantric Yoga*,
and *Yoga of Herbs*
Santa Fe, New Mexico

Many thanks to my healing teachers and the many clients
who have made this book possible.

INTRODUCTION

From the Self is born this Prana. Just as there can be this shadow when a man is there, so this Prana is fixed on the self. He comes to this body owing to the actions of the mind.

—Prasna Upanisad III.3

My own interest in pranic healing is due to a chronic back problem that I inherited. When I met my first healing teacher, I had been suffering from continuous back pain for fifteen years. At times, I just had to go to bed for a few days, but generally it was a constant pain or ache in the upper back.

At fifteen, it became apparent that I had a deformation of the spine, called idiopathic kyphoscoliosis. For two years I wore a leather-and-steel corrective brace to help straighten the curvature. It did help somewhat, as I could now make the spine into a straight line with effort. The pain that troubled me for the next fifteen years was primarily muscular. The muscles had to do the work of the spine as well as their own job, which resulted in constant fatigue.

Overworked, stressed, and tired muscles. Sound familiar? We have all had that at some point in our life. For me it was always present.

I had tried various body workers who employed different systems with mixed results. Their methods left me bruised and battered. Even "soft" work was generally too hard for me. My relief never lasted for more than a day or two. I had tried allopathic (Western medicine) treatments with limited results. I consulted acupuncturists, osteopaths, chiropractors and psychical therapists with no results.

On a friend's recommendation, I went to see Ananda, a Japanese body worker who was originally a chiropractor. He had continued his training (all of which took place in Japan) with techniques using prana. I was interested in having a session with him due to his reputation for soft work. Yet I had no expectations that anyone could help me at this point. I couldn't have been more wrong!

The first treatment left me curious, dissatisfied, and, after a day, in more pain than before. When I told him that on the next visit, his only reply was that it was a good sign. The logic at the time failed to convince me: that I was in more pain was a good sign? The session consisted of him touching me softly at certain points and staying there for long periods of time. I would feel strange electric currents flowing through my body at those times.

The second treatment was much the same as the first, only this time, I was even more dissatisfied. I am still not sure why I ever went to the third session: possibly because I had booked it and I dislike missing appointments. But it was the third treatment that changed my life.

Working with prana becomes a love affair. It is by far one of the most enjoyable things in my life. That day was the beginning of this on-going love affair. There is something so beautiful about pure energy that it is impossible to describe. Later, when I began to learn from Ananda, he would often become speechless with tears in his eyes. Such is the beauty of prana.

After the third and fourth sessions, my body no longer held pain. Ananda explained that the first and second treatments were necessary to change the energetic habit of my back. Over the years, our bodies develop habits, just as our minds do. Some of these habits are good and some are bad. My tension stemmed from a physical problem, but the result was the bad habit of holding tension (which indicates blocked prana in energetic medicine).

Eight years have now passed and I can honestly say the changes are permanent. I do have pain in my back when I ignore it and continue an action that overstresses the muscles. But the constant pain never came back. The energetic patterns have changed. If I do some simple yoga exercises, the tension immediately departs. Or at the worst, a good night's sleep will solve the problem—a problem that bothered me for fifteen years.

I was so surprised at the result that I asked Ananda what he was doing, and if I could learn to take care of myself. He answered that he was using prana (whatever that was) and yes, I could learn to heal myself. He was giving a workshop the following month, he said, and I was welcome to participate.

I worked for one year with his techniques and guidance. As I worked more with prana, my sensitivity continued to grow. My hands began to feel subtle energies outside of the physical body and my interest grew. At that time, I was practicing meditation several hours every day. I was doing a form of Vipassana, from the Buddhist tradition. In reflection, I am sure that my meditation practices accelerated my learning abilities with prana. I already had an awareness of my breath and the gap between the incoming and outgoing breaths.

There are key moments in our lives that can change their direction suddenly. Mine came at that time: the beginning of an endless love affair with that unknown force, prana. I went on to work with another teacher, Swami Chidvilas, for several years. My second teacher worked primarily on the subtle bodies. It was with his guidance that I learned the art of energetic medicine.

After several years, I began to be troubled by questions that neither of my teachers could answer. I became sure that, until I knew the answers to my questions, healing would not really happen in the truest sense of the word. At one point, I stopped work for four months in disillusionment.

Life came to my rescue by sending me a spiritual master, H.W.L. Poonja, a direct disciple of Ramana Maharishi. Over the next year, he answered every question I had. Under his guidance I went on to research many texts of the ancient seers of

India. Having unraveled many of the secrets of yogic healing, I moved to France and began practicing pranic healing.

It was in France that a woman came to me with an ovarian cyst the size of an orange. She was under medical care and had undergone a complete series of tests. She was determined to heal herself without surgery. This was not an uneducated decision; she had been a registered nurse for twenty years at our local hospital. Her doctor was supportive of her decision to try and heal herself through natural methods; if they didn't work, the only alternative was surgery.

As I scanned the region over the left ovary, my hand resting about three inches above her body, I felt the pranic congestion associated with a cyst. This one felt as though it was ready to burst. I proceeded to assist the body in its natural function—expelling the invader. I started a series of cleansing and recharging exercises for the appropriate chakras and for the ovary itself, and then balanced and charged her whole body with fresh prana. The treatment took about twenty–five minutes; then we started to talk about the causes of this disruption in her body.

My diagnosis was very favorable in her case, mainly because of her determination to heal herself. I took an immediate liking to this woman, who was convinced that surgery was unnecessary for her. Her conviction and determination would take her a long way.

We scheduled a session for her husband, something critical in this kind of illness, so that they could approach the root imbalance of the illness together. Then I suggested an herbal decoction that would help to dissolve the cyst if taken as a tea three times daily. I asked her to call me in a few days and to return in a week's time.

The woman called two days later to say that she was discharging blood mixed with some foreign matter. In her case, it was a good sign. The body was painlessly expelling the cyst in a natural way. Over the next two months, we had only four sessions before the cyst completely disappeared and her doctor pronounced her completely healthy. With her husband's support, she followed the guidelines I gave her and continued to drink the herbal tea that I recommended. After our last session, her body was still free of any pranic congestion. All the energy circuits were moving well and her general constitution was peaceful.

Is pranic healing a miracle cure for all diseases? No, it is a simple yogic method known for thousands of years that uses the life force of the body, the prana, to assist and balance the total organism. Sometimes cures are slow and sometimes they are miraculously fast. Take the example of this psychologist in San Francisco. He had been suffering from migraine headaches for several months before we met. They were debilitating, causing a loss of work and sleep. They were accompanied by severe sciatic nerve pain in the upper right leg. I was just on my way out of town for two weeks, but managed to give him a treatment before my departure. On my return, I was pleased to hear that the headache had vanished twenty–four hours after the session and had not returned. The sciatica problem had also disappeared after a day. I gave a reinforcement session for the sciatic nerve several days after my return to help maintain the new pranic currents opened in the body. His problems haven't returned to the same degree, four years later.

Or take the case of the following woman, who was troubled by a neck pain so severe that for one year she could not sleep or function normally in life. She had tried every method available in her town and was desperate. After one treatment, her pain disappeared. The next day, a friend gave her a massage and the pain returned. I gave her another treatment and the pain vanished. The pain has returned occasionally over the last three years, but it has never lasted beyond a good night's sleep. Just think: one whole year of pain and it vanished in thirty minutes!

What is this mysterious force called prana? And how can it work miracles like those described above? If it has existed for thousands of years, why are we only hearing about it now? Is this method scientific? Are there any dangers or side effects with this method? Do I need any special ability or skill to learn this method? How long will it take to learn? What illnesses can it help to cure?

These and many other questions are answered in the following pages. I have written this book because, in my studies, I have never found a book that gave the origin of energetic heal-

ing. The roots are found in the tradition of yoga. Dr. David
Frawley, in his book *Gods, Sages and Kings*,[1] presents evidence
that India's culture is possibly the oldest on the Earth. There are
many ancient Indian texts—some dating from before 5000 B.C.—
that describe how to use prana, the life force, for war, meditation, or healing.

I have made an effort to present my findings in a clear, easy-
to-read, and practical format. The first three chapters are not
critical to the method of healing, but rather to understanding
the origins of prana and energetic medicine.

None of the current books on energetic healing are founded
on or follow the scientific methods of yoga. These newer techniques were created in this century, while the methods of yoga
have existed for more than 7000 years. This book makes an
effort to dispel many of the misunderstandings that exist about
energetic medicine—misunderstandings developed in these new
schools of healing. *The method this book presents has been tested
by millions of people for thousands of years.* It still exists because it
works.

While there are many methods of energetic medicine, these
are some of the benefits unique to yogic pranic healing:

1. If you can breathe, you can heal with prana;
2. There is no set system into which different individuals must
   be fit;
3. Diseased matter can be cleansed away before energizing
   with fresh prana;
4. You can collect excess prana to energize others, rather
   than using your own prana;
5. You can cleanse your own body of unwanted or diseased
   matter collected from treatments or from other people;
6. Prana is projected from the Heart through the hands; in
   this way prana takes on the quality of love;
7. No initiations or religious rituals are needed;
8. Pranic healing complements all other forms of healing;

---

[1] Dr. David Frawley, *Gods, Sages and Kings* (Salt Lake City, UT: Passage
Press, 1991), pp. 21-36.

9. Pranic healing, part of the first system of holistic medicine, Ayurveda, was founded by sages who viewed the human being as a totality.

Pranic healing has brought not only health, but a better life, to hundreds of people that I know. I now wish to share that beauty with a greater number of people. This book is dedicated to all of the suffering people who can and will benefit from this method of healthcare.

CHAPTER 1

WHAT IS PRANA?

Spirituality is nothing more than understanding this play of consciousness—try to find out what this fraud is by seeking its source.

—Sri Nisargadatta Maharaj

There is an ancient story about prana from the *Prasna Upanishad*.[1] A group of spiritual seekers approached a teacher for supreme knowledge. The teacher agreed to answer their questions if they remained for one year in meditation as celibates. This was asked so that they could gain control over their senses. They agreed. After a year had passed, one of them asked: "From what are all beings born?" The answer was given that consciousness, wishing to enjoy itself, created opposites, matter and energy, with the idea that these two would produce all beings. Prana, energy, is depicted as the Sun and matter is depicted as the Moon. These opposites, energy and matter, together created the universe.

The students asked another question: How many "deities" sustain a person, and which of these is the chief and most glo-

---

[1] *Eight Upanisads, Prasna Upanisad*, trans. by Swami Gambirananda (Calcutta: Advaita Ashrama, 1992), pp.407–503.

rious? This was the response of the teacher: How many deities (intelligent impulses) control the body, and who is the chief of these? The deities all answered together: Space said, "I am the chief," and so did Air, Fire, Water, Earth, the functions of Speech, Mind, Sight, Feeling, and Hearing. Each of them claimed that it was they who held the body together and allowed it to function.

To these deities the chief Prana said, "Do not be deluded; it is I who do not allow the body to disintegrate." The others were unbelieving. Seeing their attitude, the chief Prana started to rise above the body. Immediately, all the others followed. Then the Prana remained quiet, and all the others were quiet. Seeing the reality, all the other deities began to praise Prana as their chief. The truth is that, like the spokes on the hub of a chariot wheel, all things are fixed on the hub of prana.

The teacher then expounded this idea further. It is Prana who resides with the organs and unites all the body as a unit. Prana is worshiped as the creator, the destroyer, and the preserver of all the universe. Prana appears as the sun, as the rain, as fire, as air, as the controlling force of all the world and the heavens. Prana is honored as the all–pervading entity and lord of all creatures.

Again a student asked: "Where does this prana come from, how does it come into this body and how does it support the psychical world?" The teacher responded: "Prana comes from the Self (pure consciousness). It is attracted to the body by the mind and divides itself into five forces to govern the body. Prana functions just like a king, who allocates the work to his ministers—in this case, the five pranas who each control a region of the body."

The story, in symbolic terms, explains the nature and actions of prana. Virtually all of the ancient scriptures use metaphors and symbols to explain the knowledge derived from the sage's direct perceptions of reality. The ancient sages used a subjective method to explore and experience reality, just as scientists today use objective methods to explore reality. Both are valid methods, but, because science has yet to acknowledge prana, this manual will follow the wisdom of the ancient yogis or seers who, long ago, knew about the secrets of prana.

Prana is the vital energy of the universe. Every living being is alive due to prana. Different traditions have different names for prana: the vital force, ki, chi, orgone, and simply "energy." While prana is often associated with breath, it is not breath; prana rides on the breath, but is different from breath. Prana enters and exits the body following the movement of the breath. That is the nature of prana: movement.

The name *prana* is Sanskrit; it means before (*pra*) breath (*ana*).[2] Prana is neutral; it is pure energy without any qualities. This pure energy can take on any quality without losing its purity; just as, by putting on clothes, we associate with a style of dress, still we remain the same person.

Prana can be used to facilitate meditation, sex, combat, or healing. It gives vitality to the physical body and it also gives us the power to think. Prana is both physical and mental energy: "Movement of thought in the mind arises from the movement of prana; and the movement of prana arises because of the movement of thought in consciousness. They thus form a cycle of mutual dependence, like waves and movement of currents in water."[3] This quote is from an ancient scripture, one of the most respected in India, and is more than 5,000 years old. The information presented here is not new. A complete science built on the effects of prana has been in existence for thousands of years.

Traditionally, yoga teaches that there are five kinds of prana in the body: prana, apana, samana, udana, and vyana. There is also the cosmic all-pervading Prana, which is the source of the five pranas that are confined to the body, each with a specific function. Of the five pranas in the body, prana and apana are commonly acknowledged as the most important. Prana is seated in the heart and head; apana is seated at the base of the spine and is known as the "downward breath." Together, prana and apana form the polarity of breath. These two forces are actually what gives us the power to breath. Prana is the solar aspect

---

[2] Sri Nisargadatta, *I Am That* (Bombay, India: Chetana, 1991), App. 3.
[3] Swami Venkatesananda, trans., *Yoga Vasistha: The Supreme Yoga* (Shivanandanagar, Uttar Pradesh, India: Divine Life Society, 1991), p. 313, section 5, chapter 78, verse 14.

(masculine) and apana is the lunar aspect (feminine). Of the other pranas, samana is seated in the region of the navel and is known as the "upward breath"; udana is centered in the throat but moves up and down the whole body; and vyana is diffused throughout the body, holding it all together.[4] Throughout this book, we will refer to all five pranas simply as prana; when cosmic Prana is intended it will be capitalized.

Pranic healing is a branch of yoga, which is one of the Vedic sciences. What exactly is yoga? There are many different branches of yoga, some dealing with the body, some with the mind, some with occult powers, and some with self–realization or enlightenment.

Originally, the ancient seers were proficient in all the known sciences: Ayurveda (medicine), yoga postures, meditations, mathematics, astrology, geology, war, and religion. These were called the Vedic sciences. Normally a sage would specialize in one field, but was expected to know the fundamentals of all eight branches of knowledge. Ayurveda, hatha yoga, and pranayama were concerned with the physical body. Pranic healing came from this branch of the Vedic tradition.

Generally, yoga is understood to be a method by which a "union" with the divine or God is achieved. Although one can practice hatha yoga without being aware of the divine, this is not really yoga in its purest sense, but simply an Indian method of exercise to maintain physical health. If, however, we practice hatha yoga knowing that mind, prana, and the body arise from a source unknown to us, and search for that unknown source, that is yoga in its purest meaning.

It is not the method or the practice that is yoga; rather it is our search for that unknown source that is yoga. Pranic healing is simply a method; it can also be used as yoga, to lead us to the source of our vital force and the source of all that exists.

Yoga, as used in this book, is the tradition of sages and texts that lead one from the body, the manifestation, to the ultimate, beyond both the manifest and the unmanifest. "I salute the Supreme Self. It was the Self which first taught the brilliant

---

[4] Sir John Woodroffe, *The Serpent Power* (Madras, India: Ganesh & Co., 1989), p. 77.

knowledge of Hatha Yoga. Hathayoga was given as a ladder so he who has the desire may climb to the highest state of Rajayoga."[5]

Pranic healing is a nonviolent approach to health that anyone can learn, nonaggressive to the body, the mind, and the emotions. There is no interference with the individual, no system, no classification. By energizing the body, prana revitalizes it naturally, enabling it to fight off illness and maintain good health. This is a method of healing that has existed almost as long as mankind, a method totally natural to the human race. Pranic healing is a holistic approach; in other words, it revitalizes the complete human organism—body/mind/emotion. True healing must work, not only on the manifested disease, but on the root problem to be really effective.

The Relationship of Prana and Mind

Prana has a natural movement, as does mind. What is mind exactly? Mind is the process of thoughts rising and falling, or appearing and disappearing, in consciousness that is commonly referred to as "thinking."

Mind is a series of thoughts. Mind and prana are two aspects of the same phenomenon; both exist together and are inseparable. Prana is the principle of movement and mind is the principle of intelligence. Therefore, all actions require prana, including thinking. By slowing down the breath, the thoughts are slowed down. Yoga's pranayama, an effective meditation technique, uses this understanding to still the ever–active mind. "[B]y control of the life-force the mind is also restrained: even as the shadow ceases when the substance is removed, the mind ceases when the life-force is restrained." [6] This understanding is the basis of all esoteric healing. The consequences of mind and

[5] Kevin & Venika Kingsland, trans., *Hathapradipika* (England: Grael Communications, 1977), p.15, verse 1.
[6] Swami Venkatesananda, *Yoga Vasistha: The Supreme Yoga*, p. 229, section 5, chapter 13, verse 83.

energy being completely interdependent are so vast that few of us realize the potential.

Consciousness, as used here, is synonymous with Existence, Source, Self, Love or God. Mind is often confused with Consciousness. Mind is that of which consciousness is aware. What then is consciousness? "We may roughly put it like this. Existence or consciousness is the only reality. Consciousness plus waking, we call waking. Consciousness plus sleep, we call sleep. Consciousness plus dream, we call dream. Consciousness is the screen on which all the pictures come and go." [7]

---

[7] Sri Ramana Maharshi, *Be As You Are*, ed. David Godman (New Delhi: Penguin Books India, 1992), p. 14.

CHAPTER 2

THE HUMAN BODIES

As the light [pure awareness] pervades the entire body, one gets attached to the body, mistakes the body for the Self and regards the world as different from oneself.

—Sri Ramana Gita

There is only one human body; however, there are layers that vibrate at different frequencies. The finer layers, or higher-frequency layers, have an effect on the lower-frequency layers until, at last, this reaches the physical layer, which vibrates at the lowest frequency. This is the simplest explanation of the complete human body.

Another way to look at it is to imagine five circles of paper, each one larger than the last. Lay them all together in a pile and hold them up to the light. The area where they all overlap is the most dense; that is the physical body (see figure 1, page 8). It is a misconception to think of the bodies as being separate from one another; they are interdependent and cannot be separated. As long as the individualized consciousness or ego exists, there is this combined body.

This ego-body is known in yoga as the subtle body (puryastaka, or ativahika[1]). Traditionally, yoga speaks of three

[1] Swami Venkatesananda, *Yoga Vasistha: The Supreme Yoga*, (Shivanandanagar, Uttar Pradesh, India: Divine Life Society, 1991), p. 384, section 6, chapter 1, verse 31.

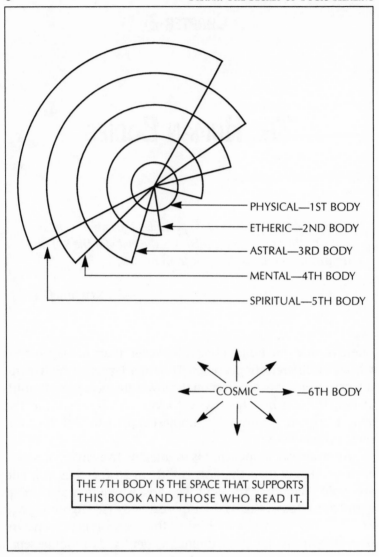

PHYSICAL—1ST BODY
ETHERIC—2ND BODY
ASTRAL—3RD BODY
MENTAL—4TH BODY
SPIRITUAL—5TH BODY

COSMIC—6TH BODY

THE 7TH BODY IS THE SPACE THAT SUPPORTS
THIS BOOK AND THOSE WHO READ IT.

Figure 1. Cross section of the bodies.

bodies and five "sheaths": gross, subtle, and causal bodies; and the material, vital, mental, intellectual and blissful sheaths.[2] The name *sheath* is used in yoga, because each sheath covers the pure essence of consciousness that is the undying reality (see figure 2, page 10).

The system that I use is not different in reality, but only in terminology. It consists of seven bodies and fits modern usage. The first body is the physical; the second is the etheric (vital or energetic); third is the astral (or emotional); the fourth is the mental; fifth is the spiritual (or intellectual); the sixth is the cosmic (often called pure intelligence, as there is still an individual consciousness); and the seventh is impossible to name, as it is beyond both name and form (see figure 3, page 11).

"A notion entertained by consciousness appears as the body," the *Yoga Vasistha* explains. "It has a corresponding subtle body (puryastaka or ativahika) composed of mind, intellect, ego-sense, and the five elements. The self is formless, but the puryastaka roams in this creation in sentient and insentient bodies until it purifies itself, lives as if in deep sleep and attains liberation."[3]

I have studied most of the systems of the human body and favor this terminology as matching my own experience in healing, meditation, and the altered states of mind. When I have no thoughts, there isn't any body or bodies, only consciousness. It requires a mind to maintain the existence of the bodies. Often, these systems give erroneous information about the bodies, because the person or persons relating them have never left mind or subtle mind. Even channeled information, or information from entities without a physical body, is subtle mind and therefore questionable.

I personally trust the system of yoga for two reasons: it has existed for thousands of years and has been tested over and over; and it matches my own experience. Although I may use modern terminology, this book follows the ancient yogic tradition.

---

[2] *Advaita Bodha Deepika*, trans. by Swami Ramanananda Saraswati (Tiruvannamalai, India: Sri Ramanasramam, 1990, p. 55.
[3] Swami Venkatesananda, *Yoga Vasistha: The Supreme Yoga*, p. 408, section 6, chapter 1, verse 51.

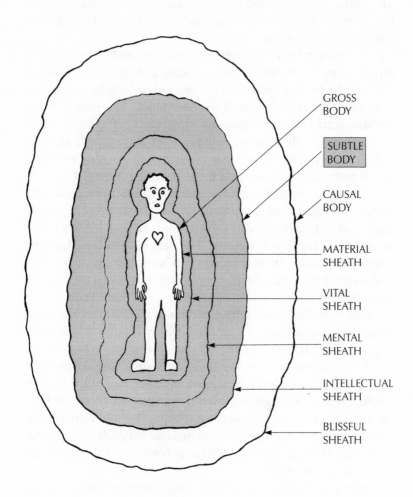

Figure 2. The three bodies and the five sheaths of yoga.

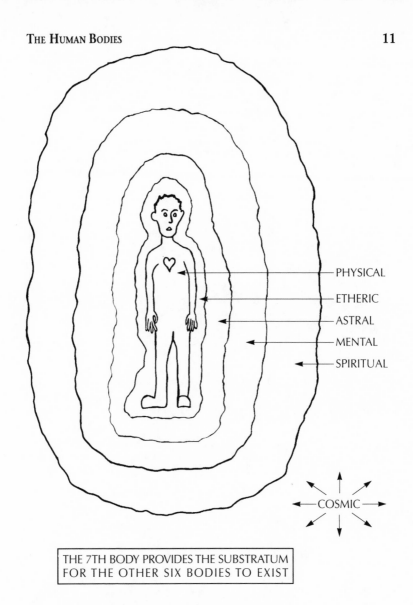

Figure 3. The seven bodies of the Western system.

Chapter 3

How Energetic Medicine Works

*Beingness has the quality to become whatever you think of.
Whatever concept you feed to the consciousness, the consciousness will provide you with that.*

—Sri Nisargadatta Maharaj

Pranic healing is also called energetic medicine. The perspective of energetic medicine is that disease is a disorder in the subtle bodies or the *nadis* (Sanskrit for the subtle channels that carry the prana throughout our bodies). There are over 72,000 nadis, according to one school of yoga, and they are located in the etheric body.

Normally, we feel these disorders as pains or tensions, which in later stages can manifest as illness. The practitioner of pranic healing can eliminate pain, tension, and illness by cleansing and recharging the etheric body with prana. When the cause of the disease is of an emotional nature, the astral or emotional body must be addressed as well. The mind also affects our health. Therefore, by addressing the mental body, many disorders of a mental nature can be rectified over a period of time. In treating the subtle bodies, there may be a time lag before the effects of the work are felt in the physical body.

To effectively understand how energetic medicine works, it is important to understand the ideas from the first and second chapters: mind, prana, and the subtle bodies. In brief, mind and prana are interrelated phenomena and cannot be separated.

The etheric (vital) body is the layer of our body on which prana functions directly. It is the etheric body which absorbs and distributes the prana throughout the bodies. The etheric body is truly our vitality, consequently it is very important in pranic healing. The etheric body is aided in its work by both the nadis and the chakras. A detailed explanation of both will be given in the chapter on chakras. If for any reason the nadis or chakras are blocked, congested, or cut (as in surgery), an imbalance or illness of some kind will manifest somewhere in the body. Because the body is a complex system, it is often difficult to find the exact place of origin of the disturbance.

There are different systems to explain the different correlations between various parts of the body. In pranic healing, we approach these imbalances without any preconceived ideas or system. Using the first of the three steps of pranic healing, *detection*, we scan the etheric body of the individual to locate the root of the pranic imbalance. A problem is located through detection, energetically cleansed and then revitalized by energizing with prana. These steps can be repeated over and over, on the applicable body, organ, or as the situation dictates. This is the basis of pranic healing: to form a very complete, open approach to healthcare.

Pranic healing is a simple method for use on our family and friends to relieve colds, fevers, headaches, muscle aches and pains, bronchitis, and many other common ailments. It can also be used to heal major diseases of all kinds with the proper training. Any person with the interest to learn and the discipline to practice can heal with prana. Healing requires no special abilities. It does require daily practice for some time.

This method is not meant to replace doctors or other medical practitioners, but rather to increase the effectiveness of all forms of medicine by using the most fundamental element of life: the life force or prana.

Prana is called the vital force because it is universally available to all living things at all times. As explained earlier, prana is neutral by nature, yet has the ability to carry any quality. All rituals, rites, or deities affect the mind and thus the prana. It is the mind that attaches different qualities to the prana. A strong belief in a ritual increases the strength of the prana, not because of the ritual, but because of our firm belief in the ritual.

With this understanding, we can see that all cultural, religious, and magic healing only works through the mind to increase the flow of prana, not through some secret power. Prana is that secret power and needs nothing else to heal.

All natural healing uses prana, regardless of the practitioner's awareness of it. If the practitioner is aware of prana, then its effectiveness is greatly increased. Maximum effectiveness is achieved when the practitioner approaches each case individually without a concept or fixed system, detects the energetic bodies for a diagnosis, collects extra prana, cleanses the individual energetically, and recharges the patient with fresh, healthy, loving prana. Energetic healing is a simple, noncomplicated method of heathcare; if the presentation of a method is mysterious or complicated, it should be examined for honesty. The point here is that energetic healing is positive and true; it is sometimes the commercialization of it that is false.

CHAPTER 4

SENSITIZING THE HANDS

All beings, whether Devatas, men or animals, exist only so long as the Prana is within the body. It is the life duration of all.

—Kaušitaki Upanisad III.2

There are three basic steps in pranic healing: scanning, cleansing, and energizing. Together, these three steps can be used on the physical, second, third, and fourth bodies to alleviate pain and illness; in pranic healing, there is no fixed system in which each individual fits. By repeating these steps over and over, an individual's particular problem can be solved. With the use of these three steps, there are no limitations on the healer or the patient. Before beginning with the first step, it is helpful to sensitize the hands.

All methods of energetic healing are facilitated by sensitizing the hands. The more sensitive our hands are, the more we can feel. This is also true for body workers, chiropractors, osteopaths, and many other professionals who touch people. In pranic healing, sensitizing the hands is quite important, because there is no structure to rely on; we rely on our hands to give us the energetic messages or feelings.

In the center of our hands is a small door, commonly known as a *chakra,* that gives and receives prana. It is the development

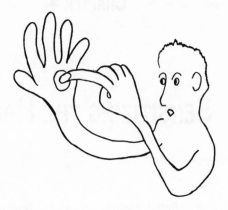

Figure 4. Activating the hand chakra.

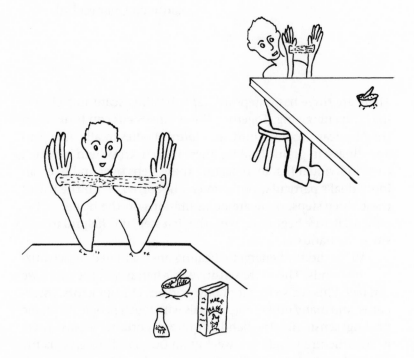

Figure 5. Exercise to sensitize the hands.

Figure 6. Sensitize the hands with a friend.

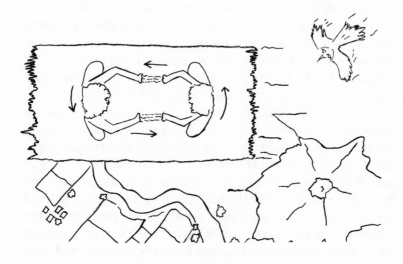

Figure 7. Prana moving in a circuit from left to right.

of this door that gives us sensitivity in our hands. The larger the opening is, the more easily the energy can flow in and out; this is having sensitized hands.

To open the door, just bring your awareness to the hand and focus your attention there. It may be easier at first to open the door by placing your finger on the center of the other hand (see figure 4, page 18). That's all there is to opening the hand chakra. Do it regularly; it is recommended that five or ten minutes a day for three or four months is sufficient to permanently activate your hands. My own experience is that the sensitivity never stops growing; it is an endless experience.

Another exercise to sensitize the hands is to hold the palms together, but not touching. Slowly, move the hands apart to a distance of about eighteen inches, then slowly move the hands together again (see figure 5, page 18). This should be done for five or ten minutes at a time. It takes several minutes for the prana to build up between the hands. Keep them together until a heat or an electric feeling is felt between them, then slowly move them apart. Normally, eight-out-of-ten people can feel the prana on the first try and most of those can immediately feel the limit of the etheric body as the hands move slowly together.

Now try this with a friend. Face each other and have your hands facing each other as well, palms flat and arms slightly bent. Repeat the same exercise with your friend; one of you stay still as the other moves toward or away from the other's hands. When the feeling is clear, trade roles so that the other can control the distance between the hands (see figure 6, page 19).

Now another variation: focus your attention only on the right hand; the prana will move out of the right hand. Slowly become aware that a circuit of prana is flowing out of your right hand and entering the left hand of the other person. It continues to flow up their arm, then moves up to their heart and down their right arm to the hand, flowing into your left hand and up to your heart area, then down and out your right hand again (see figure 7, page 19). It's easy: just focus on the right hand giving and the rest happens naturally. It may sound difficult, but it is really very easy. It is already happening; we normally just don't notice, because it is subtle.

CHAPTER 5

SCANNING OR DETECTION

All this world and everything in heaven is under the control of Prana—protecting us just as a mother does her sons, ordaining for us splendour and intelligence.

—Prasna Upanisad II.13

Scanning, or detection, is the method of diagnosis used in pranic healing. This technique of diagnosis is generally done on the subtle bodies, but can also be applied to the physical body. Scanning is easily understood: if you hold your hand next to a stove, you sense heat. Similarly, with your hand held next to the body of another person, you feel sensations.

Each person is different; everyone feels different sensations when scanning. For example, I might feel heat when you feel blowing air; or I might feel hot blowing air and you might feel prickly heat. Here are the most common sensations felt in detection: hot or cold areas; blowing air; hot or cold moving air; prickly feeling; combination of prickly feeling with all the previous sensations; or nothing at all. The art of detection lies in how to know or intuit the meaning of the different sensations.

One important factor in scanning is having a neutral mind. This requires a brief explanation. What is neutral? Neutral is not having a fixed concept or idea of what is happening with the patient, what kind of person they are, the nature of their illness, the location or cause of their illness, or any diagnostic system.

This may leave us wondering what we have left to work with. The answer is: nothing. We have nothing to work with, except a neutral mind. When the mind is neutral, or not holding a concept, the accuracy of scanning is very high. Scanning has no meaning in and of itself; it is just a neutral detection of what is in that moment.

Now we will learn the general interpretations of the common sensations. Remember, don't rely on other people's explanations; trust yourself; stay calm and neutral as you detect the subtle bodies.

HOT: Too much prana, or a congestion of prana; a leak of prana, or an infection; a serious disease if very hot; too much prana in your hands, in which case, shake or wash with cool water and try again.

COLD: Little or no prana, or a congestion/block in the surrounding area; a serious disease that is using all the available prana in the area; or your hands are not sensitized.

BLOWING AIR: Commonly, this is prana leaving the body, usually called a "leak"; can be an infection; check for fans or drafts in your work area.

HOT OR COLD MOVING AIR: A combination of any of the above.

PRICKLY OR ELECTRIC: An imbalance in the prana; can be either too much or too little; often goes with infections, blocks of prana, or a serious illness; or your hands have too much prana, in which case, shake or wash with cool water and try again.

PRICKLY/ELECTRIC COMBINED: A combination of any of the above.

NOTHING: No prana; a very fine etheric body; hands are not sensitized; or your attention is not present.

Naturally, the body has some areas that contain more prana than others. For example, after eating, more prana will be centered in the region of the stomach and intestines than in other areas. Also, certain chakras generally have more prana than others (see chapter 10). Just because we feel an abundance of "something," it does not mean that it is wrong for that person.

For example, an athlete will generally have a strong amount of prana in the middle and lower body, whereas a professor of physics will normally have an abundance of prana around the region of the brain. If the professor has just done a daily routine of exercise, more prana will be located in the lower areas of the body than the upper areas. Thus, we see the importance of not jumping to any conclusions before scanning the patient.

Scanning is the first step in pranic healing. After talking with the person to find out what is transpiring in their body, scanning should be done. If it is necessary to do a full–body diagnosis, the person should be relaxed and comfortable, which usually means lying down flat on a soft but firm surface. All of the three steps of pranic healing are facilitated by the relaxed state of the person. It is difficult to be fully relaxed in a standing position, although it is absolutely fine to carry out all these steps that way. These steps are described as if the person is lying down, because that is how I work.

A person may need only a local treatment, in which case sitting in a chair is perfectly adequate, provided the afflicted area remains readily available. The definition of a "local" treatment is that the illness is relieved or vanishes by working on one small area of the body. This is generally true for colds, headaches, burns, sprains, cuts and other simple afflictions.

Illnesses that are chronic, serious, or which stem from an emotional problem need a full-body treatment. This is due to many factors, the most obvious being that the pain or disease we feel may be caused by a block or depletion of prana in another part of the body. If in doubt, scan the entire body.

These are the steps of scanning (see figure 8, page 24):

1. Sensitize your hands;
2. Have a neutral mind;
3. Start detection at the feet and work up the body to the head, or for simple problems just detect locally;

4. Keep your hand 3 to 4 inches from the physical body;

5. Remember the areas that will need to be cleansed and charged.

Because you are detecting the energetic bodies, it is not necessary to remove clothing. Large, bulky clothing can be removed, however, as it may prevent accurate detection. It is very important to be thorough in all stages of pranic healing, especially scanning. Make sure each organ, gland, or muscle is checked; and carefully check the joints (top and sides), as they are usually congested to some degree. Remember, some areas are naturally more active than others; the use of common sense is important.

Another aspect of scanning is the quality of the prana. This is especially true when detecting the bodies that are more subtle, such as the astral and mental bodies. For example, a hot area may have the quality of an infection or of healthy abundant prana, the difference being the quality of the hotness. This is applicable to all the sensations described previously. Feeling the quality requires more practice for most people, although many women find it easy immediately. More detail on the qualities of the prana will be given in chapter 12.

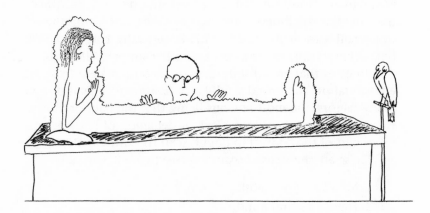

Figure 8. Scanning or detection of the etheric body.

CHAPTER 6

CLEANSING OR SWEEPING

Whoever seeks to realise the Self by devoting himself to the nourishment of the body, proceeds to cross a river by catching hold of a crocodile, mistaking it for a log.

—Vivekacudamani (verse 84)

Cleansing is so important in energetic medicine that it can stand alone without the other two steps. Yet, it is generally the least known in energetic healing.

Imagine that I want to wash the floor of my house; if I start washing before sweeping, the floor will probably be cleaner than when I started, but it may take several attempts to eliminate the dirt, which has now turned into mud. Consider how much more effective my work will be if I first sweep as much dirt as I can off the floor before washing it with soap and water. This is exactly the situation with energetic healing. Obviously, if congested or contaminated etheric matter is removed before energizing with fresh prana, the results will be much more effective.

Cleansing does several important things: it redistributes the prana throughout the body; it closes any cuts or tears in the energetic bodies; and it removes diseased etheric matter.

The most effective way to cleanse is to first collect prana, then project the prana, focusing your attention on cleansing the person. This attaches the quality of cleansing to the neutral prana.

Another name for cleansing is "sweeping," because the motion of cleansing looks just like a sweeping motion (see figure 9). There are two kinds of cleansing, general and local. Both use the same method of sweeping and are used at different times or in combination with each other.

General cleansing is a sweeping motion that starts from the top of the head and continues down to the bottom of the feet. Three or four passes down the body is sufficient. This method is very strong and should not be over-done, as the patient's vitality may drop.

It is very important to flick your hands at the end of each pass, like shaking off water from the ends of your fingers. This is true for both general and local cleansing. By flicking the hands after each pass, all diseased etheric matter is thrown off. This prevents any diseased prana or etheric matter from entering your body. Remember: prana is neutral, but it can carry anything, healthy or diseased matter.

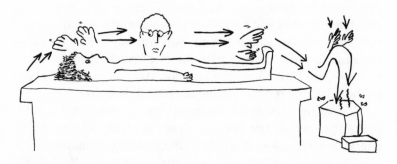

Figure 9. Sweeping or cleansing the etheric body.

DISPOSAL OF CONTAMINATED ETHERIC MATTER

What happens to the etheric matter we flick off our hands? There are three possibilities: it will go back onto the person; it will go onto us; or it will stay in the room until it attaches to another person.

Of these, the first is the most common, followed by the second. The third is less common, but rooms very definitely accumulate vibrations of etheric matter. Therefore, it is necessary to dispose of etheric matter removed from patients. There are two methods: water with salt or burning the matter with focused attention and prana.

Salt is a well-known purifier on all levels of the body. It has the ability to dissolve etheric matter. Water is a conductor which will hold or transfer energy. This is demonstrated by electricity, which is a gross manifestation of prana. Place water and salt in a bucket or bowl and flick your hands into it after each pass of sweeping. Dispose of the water after each treatment by flushing it down the toilet; the sewer is an appropriate place for contaminated etheric matter.

Using your attention to dissolve etheric matter with fresh prana is another method of disposal. This is generally an advanced method, because a very focused attention is required to effectively burn the contaminated matter. Simply flick your hands so that the etheric matter is thrown off, then give prana with your attention on burning the matter to be dissolved. Again, it is very important to be thorough, as it reflects a clear mind and focused attention. This will be emphasized over and over in pranic healing.

CLEANSING THE WORK AREA

Cleansing the area of work is equally important. I automatically cleanse my work area after each treatment by focusing my attention and directing a strong beam of prana out of my hands with the quality of purifying and cleansing. Prana and mind

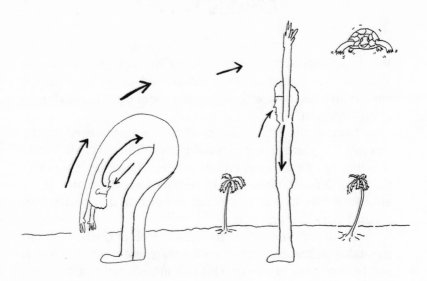

Figure 10. Self-cleansing—slow inhalation.

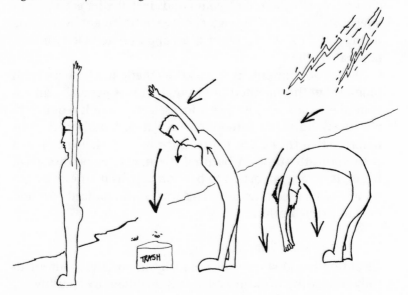

Figure 11. Self-cleansing—fast exhalation.

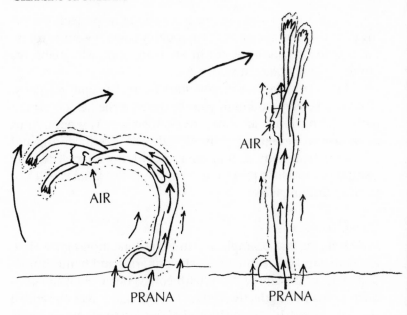

Figure 12. Self-cleansing—inhalation with ground prana

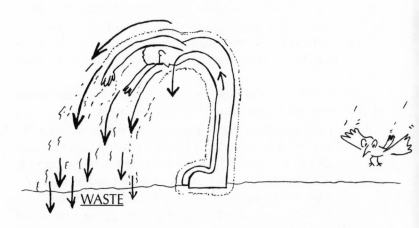

Figure 13. Self-cleansing—rapid exhalation throwing off etheric matter.

follow each other; holding purifying thoughts projects purifying prana. I am very careful to thoroughly cover the entire room. I also keep a dry bowl of salt in my workroom, which absorbs anything I may have missed.

This is no joke: when you start to treat people regularly, you must be very careful of your health and the health of your patients. The Sun is an excellent disinfectant, as is eucalyptus oil or sage burnt regularly. I use sandalwood incense during and after each treatment, as it also has a purifying effect. Use only natural products for purifying, as man-made products will not have a purifying effect.

SELF-CLEANSING
Self-cleansing is also simple, but must be done thoroughly. First, after any kind of treatment, wash your arms and hands immediately from the elbow down with cold water. Cold water conducts prana more effectively than hot water. It is recommended that you take a shower at the end of the day to wash the whole body clean of any etheric matter.

This is a very effective way of self-cleansing. Start by standing; bend over to touch your toes; slowly inhale as your hands rise up your legs, torso, chest, and finally over your head (see figure 10, page 28). Now, holding your breath, stretch your hands up as far as possible, keeping your feet flat on the ground, and with an exhalation throw your upper body down to the starting position, your hands touching your feet (see figure 11, page 28).

On inhaling, as you raise your hands, imagine prana rising up through your feet and following the movement of your hands until reaching the outstretched position (see figure 12, page 29). Then, as you exhale, imagine all the prana being thrown off as your whole body is "flicked" down to the earth (see figure 13, page 29). Repeat three to four times, or until you feel normal.

By taking prana up from the earth and then throwing it back, your body is cleansed. Also, any extra prana that is not needed after a treatment is thrown off. A mistake I made in the first years was overcollecting prana. I would feel great for a few hours after a treatment or treatments, then I would be overwhelmed by fatigue. A short nap would usually remedy this, but it took me some time to discover the mistake I was making. I had concluded that I was not collecting enough prana, when actually I was overcollecting for my system. If a sudden wave of fatigue overcomes you after a treatment, two possibilities exist: undercharging or overcharging. The second method of throwing off extra prana and cleansing your own subtle body alleviates the problem of overcharging or unwitting contamination from a patient.

CHAPTER 7

ENERGIZING WITH PRANA

Just as fire, though one, having entered the world, assumes separate forms in respect of different shapes. Similarly, the Self inside all beings, though one, assumes a form in respect of each shape and yet remains unmodified.

—Katha Upanisad II.ii.9

There are two main methods of collecting and projecting the prana; attention and breath. Using the breath and attention methods together to accelerate and amplify the prana is not necessary, but it is really much more effective than just using attention alone.

ATTENTION METHOD OF COLLECTION AND PROJECTION

In order to give prana, we must first collect some extra prana. Not to collect extra prana is to use your own, and thereby diminish your own vitality. That leaves your body open to disease or infection. This is a very common mistake made by people for whom healing is natural, who have not been alerted to the dangers of draining their vitality.

Understanding the mechanism of how prana is collected and transferred is simple and easy. Because mind and prana are interconnected, just willing or holding the intention to collect prana is enough. The knowledge that mind and prana follow each other will be used again and again in this manual.

Naturally, extra prana accumulates in the region of the navel or, for my body, just below the navel. The region of the solar plexus is another natural area of collection. Everyone is made slightly differently. What may be true for me may not be true for you; that is why there is no system in yogic pranic healing.

A reservoir of prana should be accumulated at the start of a treatment for two reasons: 1) to avoid using your own prana, thereby affecting your heath, and 2) to prevent disease or sickness from entering your body. Simply focusing your attention for the prana to collect in your body is enough; a clear strong thought is the key. The stronger the thought, the stronger the prana.

To project prana, the same rule applies: fix your attention on the prana leaving your hands. What does it mean to use your attention? It simply means that a very clear thought is present. Focusing once is enough if the thought is very clear. It is helpful not to let the mind wander; when the mind wanders, bring it back with a very clear thought of projecting prana. When the mind wanders, whatever the thoughts are, they will be carried by the prana to the patient.

The clarity of your thoughts projects clear, strong, clean, and calm prana. A confused mind will send confused prana or not collect a sufficient amount for storage. A disciplined mind is very helpful in all forms of healing; pranic healing is no exception.

BREATH METHOD OF COLLECTION & PROJECTION

Breathing is a polarity; incoming and outgoing. Prana rides on this polarity. By introducing three simple techniques to your breathing, you can at least triple the strength of the prana. These methods are: 1) retention of breath between the outgoing and the incoming breath, and between the incoming and outgoing breath; 2) being aware that the prana is moving with the breath; and 3) complete breathing or using the full capacity of your lungs.

The time of holding the breath between the polarities is very important, but doing it for one or two seconds is enough. By holding the breath, an atomic reaction occurs with the prana, thereby allowing the body to absorb greater quantities. Holding the breath for too long is not really beneficial to healing. Although it has other uses for hatha yoga or meditation, it should only be practiced under the guidance of a competent teacher. If done incorrectly or in excess, it can have a negative effect on your health.

The most effective way to breathe for healing is complete breathing.

1. Place your hands on your lower abdomen, just below the navel;
2. Inhale a breath into the lower abdomen, moving your hands slightly out as the diaphragm pushes the organs in the abdominal region down;
3. Now that your lower abdomen is full of air, continue to breathe in an upward motion to the heart area;
4. Stop for a second or two when the heart area is full;
5. Exhale slowly from the heart, out through the arms and hands;
6. Stop for a second or two;
7. Repeat for five to ten minutes (see figure 14, page 36).

At first, it may be helpful to follow the movement of the breath with your hands, starting at the lower abdomen, rising to the heart. Then from the heart move your hands out in a horizontal motion and slowly down to the lower abdomen (see figure 15, page 36). The lower abdomen is the center of our physical equilibrium. This is well known in the martial arts. Therefore, by breathing in the abdomen, you stay firmly rooted in your body. And, as stated earlier, this prevents the loss of your own vitality.

Breathing in this way does two things: it builds up your natural reservoir in the lower abdomen and solar plexus area,

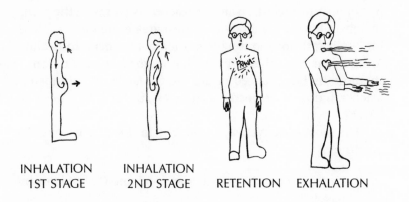

INHALATION 1ST STAGE   INHALATION 2ND STAGE   RETENTION   EXHALATION

Figure 14. Pranic breathing, or complete breathing.

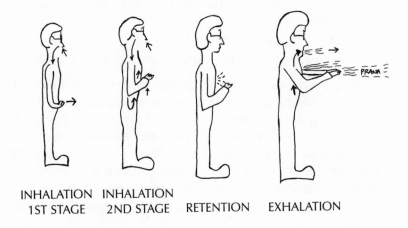

INHALATION 1ST STAGE   INHALATION 2ND STAGE   RETENTION   EXHALATION

Figure 15. Pranic breathing with the hands.

and it takes the prana up through the heart before leaving through the hands. Breathing through the heart gives the neutral prana the quality of your Heart, the seat of love or consciousness in the physical body.

By breathing in this fashion throughout the treatment you accomplish the following: you give high quality, loving prana to the patient; you stay rooted in your own body; you keep a reservoir of prana for your own health; and you keep your attention fixed on the healing treatment.

ENERGIZING OTHERS

After scanning and cleansing, it may be necessary to energize the patient. Many cases are remedied by cleansing alone. For those cases that need energizing, it is important to always verify your work by "rescanning" the areas. This is why pranic healing has no fixed system. By rescanning after each step, our work is verified. We then have two options: to energize, or to clean off the extra energy. Normally, it is necessary to repeat these three steps—scanning, energizing, and cleansing—over and over. Energizing adds prana, cleansing removes prana; this is how you can regulate the amount of prana needed for each patient.

How do I give prana to another? I use the complete breath method to collect and transmit the prana to others. It may seem a bit difficult at first to breath in the manner described above, but that is just the awkwardness of a new method. It will become second nature in a short time. When it does, giving prana will be so natural that you will wonder why you never realized it was happening before.

If by cleansing and energizing, an area is not completely calm and healthy, leave it for five or ten minutes, then return to check again. Usually, it will have changed by itself; then a little more cleansing and energizing may complete the work. There are cases when an area will not be cleansed easily. Leave it. Never force anything. (See chapter 13 for an explanation of the nature of illness.)

In pranic healing, we transmit the neutral prana with the love of the Heart. Love is not forceful or violent, therefore it is impossible to force anything to leave with prana transmitted with love. If there is a forcing or a personal investment in healing the person, it is not pranic healing or loving. It is an ego trip.

CHAPTER 8

PRANA
IN THE PHYSICAL BODY

No mortal lives by Prana or Apana; but all live because of that something else, by which these two are supported.

—Katha Upanisad II.ii.5

The physical body has a primary flow of prana from the feet to the head or from the head to the feet, depending on the person and the time of day. There are several other subcurrents of prana that exist as secondary flows. These currents or flows of prana travel in channels or circuits called *nadis* in yoga or *meridians* in acupuncture.

For most right-handed people, the main secondary flow enters from the left side and exits out the right side. Generally, for left-handed people, everything energetic is reversed. Before starting any work, verify with detection which way the circuits are moving.

There are numerous subcircuits in the body; both yoga and traditional Chinese medicine offer detailed explanations, so we will not explain more than the primary and secondary circuits for pranic healing. Anyone wishing to know about the finer circuits should study them separately, as they are too complex a subject for this brief explanation and not necessary for general healing.

The primary flow enters through both feet and rises up through each of the six major chakras before exiting through the crown of the head or it enters the crown and descends through the six main chakras to the feet (see figure 17, page 41). This is the main polarity of energy in the manifest world: descending and ascending. The plants, animals, and Earth all derive energy (prana) in this way.

The secondary circuit can easily be verified by a neutral detection of the flow of prana at the feet. Do this by holding the hands two to four inches from the bottoms of the person's feet. Remain neutral; just scan or detect the outer layer of the etheric body on the bottoms of the feet. After two or three minutes, one of the feet will pull the hand closer and the other will feel as if it is pushing the hand away—an attraction and a repulsion; another polarity (see figure 16, page 41).

Most often, prana enters through the left-foot chakra, travels up the leg until reaching the first major chakra at the base of the spine, and then descends down the right leg, exiting through the right-foot chakra (see figure 18, page 41). This circuit is usually reversed for left-handed people and sometimes even right-handed persons will move in the reverse direction. But for the majority of people this is correct; always verify for yourself!

The secondary circuit operates through the hands and arms. Entering through the left-hand chakra, traveling up the arm and shoulder, and passing through the region of the heart, it then descends out the right shoulder, arm, and hand. This circuit is also easily verified by scanning the hands of the person (see figure 18). This is an important circuit in healing, because you are projecting prana from your hands. In pranic healing, you utilize both the primary and secondary currents of energy for giving prana.

With complete breathing, you collect prana from the air to the second chakra, draw it up to the region of the heart, and then allow it to flow out your arms and hands. There is no difference in giving with the left or the right hand when using the primary flow. There is often an idea that the left hand is

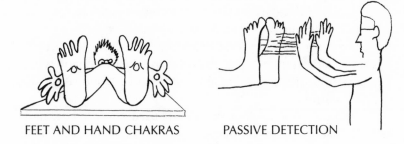

FEET AND HAND CHAKRAS   PASSIVE DETECTION

Figure 16. Detection of the secondary circuit.

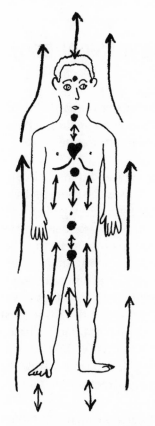

Figure 17. Primary circuit.

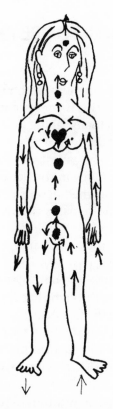

Figure 18. Secondary circuit.

more receptive than the right. This is due to the difference of the primary and the secondary circuits; either hand can be used with either circuit.

I use the left hand for receiving prana or detection myself, as that is natural for me; yet, I will also use the right hand when the situation dictates. There is no difference when using the primary current.

There are several other subcircuits used by different traditions and schools. For the beginner, the first two are quite sufficient. The prana will always find its way to the place it is needed the most, so don't concern yourself with other minor circuits at the beginning.

HOW TO USE PRANA IN THE PHYSICAL BODY

The simplest method of healing is to transfer prana by touching. This is commonly referred to as "hands-on healing." What is actually taking place is a transfer of prana from one person to another.

The easiest way to begin is by sensing the different circuits of energy in the body with the hands. This is the same method we learned in sensitizing the hands (see figure 5, page 18). One hand remains passive, the other giving prana. Remember the exercise of facing a friend, holding the palms up facing one another, one hand giving and one hand receiving prana? (Figure 6, page 19.) This is the same technique; by placing the hands at two different places on a circuit of the body, the prana will pass through that circuit to reach the other hand. This in turn opens the circuit. All of the work in the physical body is based on this method. One can proceed over the whole body, opening the circuits and thereby energizing and harmonizing the body. This is very easy to integrate with any method of massage or body work.

The technique that I usually start with is called a "neck release." This is done by placing the hands under the neck of a person who is lying down on their back. Place the finger tips between the vertebrae, starting at number seven of the cervical vertebrae at the base of the neck (see figure 19a, page 44).

Slowly exert a slight upward pressure, not lifting the neck, just applying pressure approximately one-quarter of an inch upward. Give prana; hold this for two to three minutes (see figure 19b, page 44). Very slowly relax the pressure, taking one or two minutes. This gives a feeling of falling down into the mattress; the head feels lighter, and tension is released from the neck and the base of the skull.

If you have small hands or the person has a long neck, move your hands up so that your little fingers are resting on the base of the skull and repeat (see figure 19c, page 44). I usually start and finish with this technique as it has an incredible ability to release tension and to create "new space" for future work. Do not underestimate this simple method.

My first teacher, Ananda, told a story about this technique. His master, an aged Japanese man, was approached every day for two years by a simple uneducated woman who begged to be taught a method of energetic body work. By tradition, the master could only teach a qualified student, one who had first qualified and then lived and served a master for at least four years, or until proficient in the skills the master had imparted.

The master, seeing the determination of the woman persisting two years, finally consented to teach her one method. That, he said, would be enough if she could master it. She was overjoyed.

She continued to work as a domestic housekeeper during the day and studied with the master in the evening. After two years, the master said that she had perfected the technique and could now work with people. She began a practice. After six months, she was busy. After one year, there was a line of people outside her door. After two years, she was famous in her county. After three years, she was known throughout the country. And she only knew one technique; the neck release.

The simplest technique can bring the greatest results if it is learned correctly and mastered.

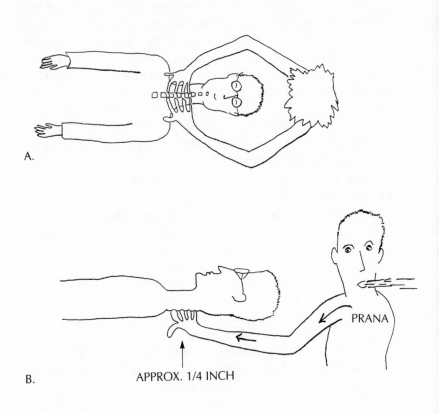

A.

B.

APPROX. 1/4 INCH

PRANA

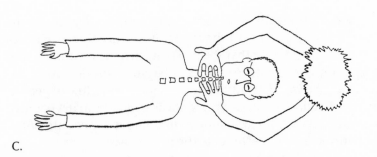

C.

Figure 19. Neck release.

STEPS IN A TREATMENT OF THE PHYSICAL BODY

By far the most direct and accurate method to determine a person's illness or pain is to ask them. Usually, we are the best system of detection for our own bodies. Always ask! This is true for working on any of the different bodies. It can also give an insight into the person's physiological make-up; how we talk about our illness gives a direct view into our basic attitudes about ourselves.

Start by having the person lie down comfortably, facing the ceiling, hands resting at their sides. Inquire about any pains or difficulties they may be having. All steps in pranic healing are facilitated by the relaxation of the person. Therefore, I some-times use relaxing music, incense, fresh flowers—anything to create a relaxing environment. Now we are ready to begin.

FRONT OF THE BODY

1. Charge yourself with prana: three to four breathing cycles is enough. Remember to breathe throughout the treat-ment, constantly maintaining a surplus of prana.

2. Relax the person and create space in the neck and head by using the neck release method; stay for four to five minutes.

3. Move to the bottoms of the feet; verify the direction that the prana is flowing in the legs and feet by detection.

4. Press the solar plexus point on the feet for three to four minutes and give prana (see figure 20, page 46). Now you can give a foot massage to stimulate all the different nadis and organs of the body, or you can give prana directly to an organ by using the reflex point on the appropriate foot.

5. If the prana is entering into the left side, start with the left leg. First place one hand on the foot and give prana, the other on the ankle and receive prana; wait until there is a current of energy between the hands.

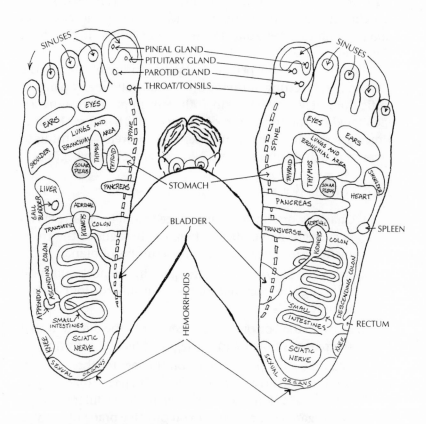

Figure 20. Pranic foot chart.

6. Move from the ankle to the knee; keep the remaining hand on the foot; wait until there is a current of energy between the hands.

7. Place the hand on the hip bone (the remaining hand is still resting on the foot giving prana) and wait until a current of energy is felt between the hands.

8. Now move the hand that was on the left hip to the right hip; continue to give prana to the left foot; wait until there is a current of energy between the hands. If the person's legs are too long for you to reach from the left foot to the right hip, give prana from the left hip to the right hip.

9. Continue down to the right knee; still give prana into the left foot or the right hip; wait for a connection between the hands.

10. Move to the ankle, then the foot. End with both hands on the feet, giving prana into the left foot and receiving it from the right foot. This has now opened the secondary circuit in the legs. Reverse this procedure if the person's current of energy moves from right to left. Always end with both feet to verify a strong healthy flow of prana. If the flow is weak, repeat steps five through ten.

11. Place one hand on the left hip and the other on the left shoulder at the base of the neck; wait until there is a connection of energy between the hands.

12. Now place one hand on the right hip and the other on the right shoulder; wait for a connection of energy. This has now opened the two main secondary nadis, the Ida, and the Pingala, that run from the base of the spine to the neck.

13. Next open the hands, arms, and shoulders. Start with the left hand (if you started with the left foot); give prana into the center of the hand; rest the other hand on the wrist; wait until there is a connection of energy between the hands.

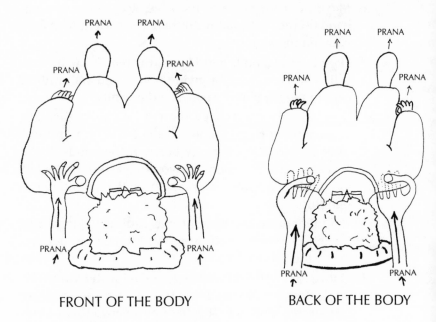

FRONT OF THE BODY   BACK OF THE BODY

Figure 21. Filling the body with prana.

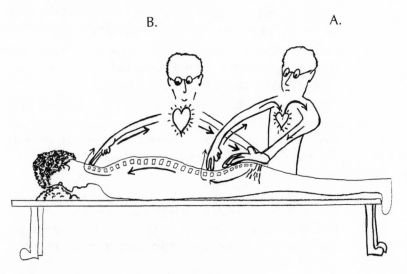

Figure 22. Energizing and cleansing the spine.

14. In this manner, move from the wrist, to the elbow, to the shoulder, to the breast bone in the center of the chest, and then over to the right shoulder, and down the right arm.

15. End with both hands. Verify the flow of prana; if it is weak, repeat steps thirteen and fourteen.

16. Next, fill the body, front and back, with prana by placing your thumbs at the base of the neck, with the four fingers spread over the collar bone. Give prana three to four minutes for each side of the body (see figure 21, page 48).

17. End with the neck release for three or four minutes. Finally, very gently place a neutral hand over the top of the head without actually touching the skull. There should be a strong healthy flow of prana exiting from the top of the head. If not, rest one hand under the neck and the other on top of the head; wait until a connection of prana is felt. Reverify with a neutral hand over the top of the head. If this has not done the trick, repeat the full treatment in two days.

BACK OF THE BODY

1. Charge yourself with prana, then start with the neck release, as in step two for the front of the body.

2. Ask the person to roll over onto their back; make them comfortable.

3. For chronic back problems, treat the feet and legs first, following the same instructions as for the front side. This is important, as many problems with the back are related to an insufficient flow of prana from the feet and legs.

4. Place a hand on the base of the spine, fingers pointing toward the head; give prana for five or six breathing cycles.

5. Keeping the hand on the base of the spine, place the other hand on the lower back, and wait for a connection of energy (see figure 22a, page 48).

DETAIL OF
FINGER POSITION

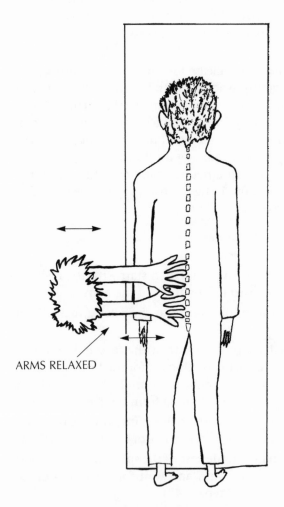

ARMS RELAXED

Figure 23. Relaxing and energizing the spine.

6. Keeping one hand on the base of the spine, move progressively up the spine, one hand-width at a time; wait for a connection between the hands before moving to the next place.

7. Finish with one hand on the base of the skull and one hand on the base of the spine (see figure 22b, page 48).

8. Have the person roll over to the starting position; do the neck release again to release any new tension that has accumulated in the neck from lying face down.

9. Lightly place a hand on the top of the head; wait until a strong flow of energy is felt coming from the top of the head.

Options: For extreme muscular tension in the back, or problems with discs, start at the base of the spine, on the left side. Place three fingers from each hand between (but not on) the vertebrae and on the tendon that is on the side of the spine. Exert a slight pressure, and slowly rock your upper body back and forth, keeping the arms slightly stiff but relaxed.

This produces a gentle rocking motion on the patient's spine; give prana for three breathing cycles while doing this. Then move up the left side so that the space between each vertebra is touched, giving prana the whole time. Now proceed up the right side in the same manner (see figure 23, page 50). This method is very effective because it sends prana between each vertebra, carrying away tension and relaxing the muscles around the cartilage. Very often a "slipped disc" will naturally come back into place with this method. Never attempt to physically manipulate a person's spine.

HINTS FOR EFFECTIVE HEALING

I always advise people to drink lots of water for two days after a treatment. This helps to eliminate toxins that have been released by the opening of the the circuits and the general recharging of the body. The movement of prana in the body will not only release the tensions and pain, but the toxins that are causing the problem as well. The more a person aids the body in the natural elimination of toxins, the less apt side effects are to occur.

If, for example, a skin rash should develop, it is usually due to toxins leaving the body. It is a good sign, just as a fever can be a good sign. However, it can be avoided if the person will drink lots of water. Toxins exit normally in three ways: the waste elimination system; the respiratory system (ie. colds, coughs and sinuses); and the skin. Do not be alarmed if for several days symptoms get worse. If, however, they persist for more than three days, or if at any time there is pain, consult a doctor or a trained practitioner of energetic medicine.

Extreme cases are very uncommon. It is, however, normal for symptoms to increase before they depart. This is common in all natural medicine; we only help the body to do its job. By reinforcing the strength of the body, natural medicine enhances its power to fight illness in the normal manner. To accelerate the illness is the direct function of natural medicine. My experience is that a common cold, if treated with prana in the first eighteen hours, will depart in forty-eight hours; if treated in the first six hours, it will depart in twenty-four hours; otherwise, seven to eight days is the normal duration for a cold. There is an old saying in France: "Do nothing with a cold and it will last a week; treat it and it will last seven days."

CHAPTER 9

KUNDALINI

Kundalini and chakras exist for beginners who practise that path of Yoga; but for the one who is practising Self-enquiry, they do not exist.

—Sri Ramana Maharshi

The subject of kundalini will invariably arise in the minds of many as we study the movement of prana in the body. Kundalini yoga is a method unto itself—a dangerous one at that—requiring intense discipline to raise the prana or sakti up through the sushumna nadi to the crown chakra. If done incorrectly, insanity or death may result. It is a very serious method, requiring a real teacher and a complete change of lifestyle. That means a sattvic (pure) diet, living in the forest, meditation, exercise during the day, and the necessity to be celibate. One book that honestly describes a traditional approach to this yoga is *The Serpent Power* by Sir John Woodroffe.[1]

Kundalini yoga claims that by mastering the primary prana in the body and by forcing it up the sushumna nadi, liberation of the Self (cosmic consciousness) will result.

---

[1] Sir John Woodroffe, *The Serpent Power* (Madras, India: Ganesh & Co., 1989).

There is another view of kundalini, quoted here by a disciple of Sri Ramana Maharshi, Sri Lakshmana Swami: "The Kundalini tradition is not speaking from the highest standpoint because it does not teach that the mind must go back to the Heart for the final realization to occur. When you speak of the kundalini rising to the sahasrara (seventh major chakra) you are speaking of a yogic state which is not the highest state. Making the kundalini rise to the sahasrara may be useful if you want siddhis (psychic powers), but it will not bring about Self-Realization."[2]

This is also supported by the *Avadhuta Gita*: "The yogi attains that eternal Supreme Atman (the highest state), which is beyond knowledge and ignorance, and which is not manifested by any such disciplines as controlling the breath, fixing the gaze, practicing postures, or exercising the nerve-current (that is, the movement of the Ida, Pingala and Sushumna)."[3]

Kundalini yoga is a valid tradition that has more to do with devotion to the Divine Mother than with the mere manipulation of prana. Dr. Frawley points this out in his book *Tantric Yoga and the Wisdom Goddesses.*[4] In the West, we are generallly unaware that kundalini is the grace of the Mother Goddess. Without the proper respect and spiritual development, kundalini yoga will only increase the concept of separation from the source of all pranas or shaktis, thus eliminating any possibility for Self–realization.

My own experience is that it takes mind to do the exercises to raise the kundalini; and the experiences I had of the kundalini were perceived by some form of subtle mind—the obvious conclusion being that it is not different from subtle mind.

When I questioned my guru about such phenomena, his reply was that "what comes and goes is not eternal, therefore is not real." Because my experience is that this phenomenon is transient, it can, at best, be only relatively real; that is, the moment it is happening it is "real." In either case, it is another manifestation of prana in the body, but not one needed for pranic healing.

---

[2] *No Mind, I am the Self,* ed. David Godman (Nellore District, A.P., India: Sri Lakshmana Ashram, 1988).

[3] Dattatreya, trans. Swami Chetanananda, *Avadhuta Gita* (Calcutta, India: Advaita Ashrama, 1988), p. 51, verse.II.35.

[4] Dr. David Frawley, *Tantric Yoga and the Wisdom Goddesses* (Salt Lake City, UT: Passage Press, 1994), pp. 30–31.

CHAPTER 10

WHAT IS A CHAKRA?

Mind is the language of the vital breath. That mind-language will talk about the impressions it has collected. The knowledge "I Am" is not a thought but observes the thoughts.

—Sri Nisargadatta Maharaj

Translations of the Sanskrit word *chakra* are common. One well-known translation is "wheel." This is not incorrect, but it is somewhat lacking as a definition. A more descriptive translation might be: "a whirling mass of energy." The traditional yogic scriptures often describe chakras as lotus flowers with different numbers of petals to represent different states of consciousness. In healing, a chakra is a distribution point of prana.

There are many ways to approach the chakras. Each layer of the body or the mind presents a different aspect of a chakra. In other words, a chakra can be approached from a physical level, or from an emotional level, or both. Traditionally, one could also approach them from a spiritual level, an energetic level, or a mental level.

How many chakras are there? The definition of a chakra is that it is determined by an intersection of two or more nadis. There are over 72,000 nadis; this certainly gives an idea of how many chakras there may be in the body.

The system of yoga agrees that there are seven main chakras, so determined by the number of nadis intersecting at a given point. Then there are twenty-one minor chakras, classified as such because of fewer nadis intersecting at their location. For the purposes of this book, it is not necessary to further define chakras, although there are many lesser points of intersection that can be useful in healing.

What is the function of a chakra? It depends on the level at which we approach the chakra. But one definition holds true as long as the physical body is alive. At the physical level, a chakra is a "pumping station" for prana. That means that the chakra distributes the prana throughout the body via the nadis. For the first two bodies, the etheric and the physical, this definition is extremely important and remains constant. By understanding the chakras in this manner, you can help the body circulate the prana more effectively, thereby maintaining and increasing your health.

You can use the chakras to give vitality and good health. In hatha yoga, different *asanas*, or physical postures, are practiced to promote the circulation of prana in different nadis and chakras. Likewise, pranayama, the practice of controlling the breath, gives good health and mind control. If done correctly, pranayama keeps the prana moving freely throughout the body.

SYSTEMS OF CHAKRAS

So much has been written about the chakras that one may wonder why it is necessary to explore them again. I find that it is necessary, mainly due to certain half-truths in circulation at the present.

While I make no claim to be an "expert" on chakras, it should be clear to anyone researching texts on yoga why so much mystery and misinformation surfaces. The primary reason is that the metaphors used in the ancient texts are difficult to understand and translate, as they are multi-dimensional.

Even the best Sanskrit scholars differ in their translations. This is clearly addressed by Sir John Woodroffe in his book *The Serpent Power*, a translation of tantric yogic scriptures about kundalini yoga and the chakras. As he states on page four of his introduction, "Generally its authors and others have purported to give what they understood to be the Hindu theory of the matter (the chakras), but with considerable inaccuracies."[1]

Woodroffe goes on to dismantle C. W. Leadbeater, a theosophist and author of *The Chakras*.[2] This book is the most used reference in the occidental world on the subject of chakras. According to Sir Woodroffe, who is very well respected in India for his honest translations of the tantric scriptures, Mr. Leadbeater has created his own explanations of the chakras. He has mixed what he calls "his own experience" and the yogic texts to create something new. It is interesting that the classic book on chakras in the Western world is, at best, a mixture of half-truths according to the yogic texts that have existed for thousands of years.

The utilization of the chakras is different in the ancient yogic texts from what is now understood in the Western world. The Western system of chakras tends to utilize them for psychoanalysis, interpreting them through Freudian/Jungian psychology. Some systems use the chakras for different levels of consciousness and physical health. But usually, they are mixed together without a clear differentiation between schools. Yoga, on the other hand is very precise and scientific.

The yogic utilization of the chakras is as follows: physical health, energetic phenomena, latent impressions stored energetically, psychic powers, and transcending of the phenomenal world. It is important not to confuse the two systems; it is much better to keep them separate. Use either when applicable, yet separately. It is my observation that this is the cause of much confusion.

---

[1] Sir John Woodroffe, *The Serpent Power* (Madras, India; Ganesh & Co., 1989), p. 4.
[2] Charles W. Leadbeater, *The Chakras* (Wheaton, IL: Theosophical Publishing House, 1973).

In classical yoga, one needed to train for years with a yogi in order to use the chakras as a guide to various states of consciousness. Kundalini yoga is, in fact, this method. A student needs to be celibate, to live in pristine nature, to eat only once a day, to sleep no more than three hours, and to spend the rest of the time meditating. I think we can safely rule out the use of chakras as a method for reaching "higher consciousness" in today's world, simply because we could not fulfill even two of these conditions, much less all five. True, one can use the information handed down as a guide to the levels of consciousness, but not as a practical method.

Here is the basic difference between yoga and the West. Western systems believe the mental process to be real, and interpret everything through that concept. Yoga, on the other hand, views the mental process as a phenomenon in consciousness, placing the reality on the substratum of consciousness rather than on the manifestations that arise out of it, subtle or gross.

Because of this basic difference, yoga uses every situation or method to try and go through the phenomenal to the source or substratum, whereas the Western systems never go to the source of the mind and phenomena, but remain in intellectual or psychological interpretations.

It is the physical and the psychological aspects of the chakras that we are concerned with in this manual, not the spiritual. Therefore, we will not address the subject of "higher consciousness" any further in relation to the chakras. The psychological aspects of the chakras are clarified later in this chapter. The physical aspects have been well-documented in other works, but for simple reference they are presented here again.

CHAKRAS AT THE PHYSICAL LEVEL

Each major chakra controls a portion of our body and is therefore responsible for the vitality and health of that region. By working directly on a chakra, we can increase the health or help to heal disease in the area that is controlled by that particular chakra.

Because the chakras are "pumping stations" of prana, it is very important that they function properly. If for any reason a chakra should malfunction, the organs controlled by that chakra will suffer due to lack of prana. Almost every illness can be treated by a chakra or combination of chakras.

There is a common misunderstanding relating to the movement of the chakras. Chakras absorb and distribute prana; they are usually in motion, either drawing in fresh prana or throwing out unwanted prana. This manifests as a rotating motion. It is normal for a chakra to rotate in both directions, and to pause between changes of rotation. One direction of rotation is taking prana in, and the other direction is throwing prana out. It is even normal for a chakra to stop for a short time, usually during sleep or rest. A healthy chakra actually rotates in an oval rather than a circle. This is due to the prana rising and falling in the body.

The seventh chakra receives and sends prana in an upward and downward direction. The other six chakras send and receive in four directions: up and down, and forward and backward. It is impossible to make a system out of the rotations, because every individual is different. Generally, a clockwise rotation is pulling prana in, and a counter-clockwise motion is pushing prana out, of the body. But this is so general that I hesitate even to state it. People cannot be categorized into systems. The phenomenon can be verified however, with a passive pendulum, one that is not influenced by our intentions, such as the stone moldavite (do not use wood or crystals), held over the second chakra for twenty or thirty minutes. It may take less time; but if we truly wait long enough, the chakra will demonstrate the motion described.

What I have listed as the location of the major chakras is different from that given in traditional yoga (see figure 24, page 60). I have used this Western system because it is more common today (see figure 25, page 61). The diseases and treatments listed in this book are all for the "Western system" of the chakras.

The other chakras have not disappeared, but simply are not the controlling chakras for this time, this environment and this industrialized world. It would seem that man in his evolution

WEST AND

EAST

Figure 24. The chakras—East and West.

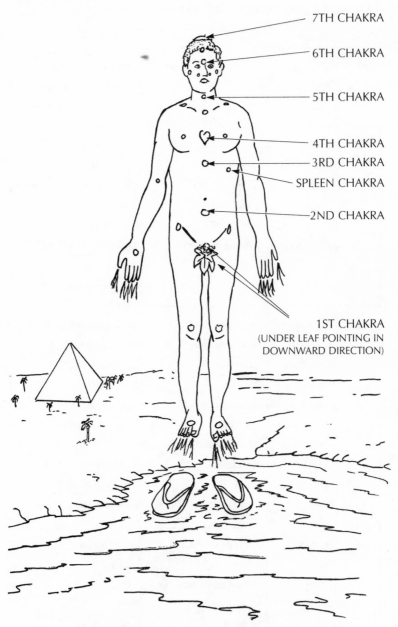

7TH CHAKRA

6TH CHAKRA

5TH CHAKRA

4TH CHAKRA

3RD CHAKRA

SPLEEN CHAKRA

2ND CHAKRA

1ST CHAKRA
(UNDER LEAF POINTING IN
DOWNWARD DIRECTION)

Figure 25. Major and minor chakras—Western system.

TABLE 1. MAJOR CHAKRAS USED IN HEALING.

Chakra	Location	Related Functions	Related Diseases
First	Pubic area (front)	Sexual organs Bladder Legs Vitality of physical body	Low vitality Weak or infected bladder Physical problems with sexual organs

	Base of spine (back)	Sexual organs
		Energizes spine
		  and body
		Control of legs
		Control of growth
		  in children
			Low vitality
			Certain cancers–Leukemia
			Allergies
			Blood diseases
			Back problems
			Physical sexual problems
			Psychological disorders

Second	Below navel and above pubic bone (front)	Large intestine Small intestine Ovaries Testicles	Intestinal troubles Sexual problems Birthing difficulties Appendicitis
	The back of the second chakra is just behind the front	Kidneys Adrenal glands Intestines Spine Blood pressure	Kidney problems General weakness Adrenal malfunction Intestinal troubles Back problems
Third	Front and back are located at the region of the Solar Plexis	Nervous system in lower body Body temperature Small intestines Stomach	Liver problems Ulcers Diabetes Spleen Gall bladder

TABLE 1. MAJOR CHAKRAS USED IN HEALING (CONTINUED).

Chakra	Location	Related Functions	Related Diseases
		Liver and spleen Gall bladder Pancreas Diaphragm	Pancreas Small intestinal problems Fevers
Fourth	Front and back are at the center of chest between nipples	Heart Thymus Circulatory system Lungs	Heart disease Children's diseases Lung problems Asthma Circulatory problems
Fifth	Front and back are at the neck, below Adam's apple	Throat Thyroids Parathyroids Vocal chords	Throat problems Vocal chord disorders Thyroid diseases
Sixth	Above and between eyebrows (front) Base of skull (back)	Control of pineal gland Hypophysis (pituitary gland) Controls endocrine system Sinuses Eyes and ears	Colds Headaches Loss of balance Endocrine malfunctions Sinus/ear/eye problems Allergies Some forms of cancer
Seventh	Top of head	Control of brain Pituitary gland	Headaches Endocrine malfunctions Loss of memory Psychological problems Nervous system disorders

TABLE 2. MINOR CHAKRAS USED IN HEALING.

Chakra Location	Related Functions	Related Diseases
Forehead at the hairline	Nervous system Endocrine system	Paralysis Loss of memory Epilepsy
Base of the throat between the collar bones (in yoga, this is the 5th chakra)	Top area of the lungs Throat	Cough Bronchitis Asthma Throat diseases
In front of earlobes	Ears Sinuses	Ear and sinus disorders Colds Headaches
Top of nose, under eyebrows, left and right sides	Sinuses	Colds Allergies
Base of nose, at nostrils left and right	Sinuses	Colds Allergies
Spleen on left side just below the ribs	Collecting prana for endocrine system General vitality	Vitality Detoxifying body
Navel	Intestines	Intestinal problems
Perineum, in front of anus (in yoga this is the first chakra)	General health of physical body Vitality Bone structure	General health Vitality

TABLE 3. TRADITIONAL LOCATIONS OF THE CHAKRAS.

Chakra	Yogic Name	Location	Flow of Prana
First	Muladhara (root place)	Perineum, in front of the anus	Up & down
Second	Svadistana (dwelling place of the Self)	Pubic bone & base of the spine	Up & down Front & back
Third	Manipura (city of jewels)	Navel region	Up & down Front & back
Fourth	Anahata (unstruck, or before sound)	Heart region	Up & down Front & back
Fifth	Visuddha (purify)	Base of neck	Up & down Front & back
Sixth	Ajna (command, to receive)	Between the eyebrows	Up & down Front & back
Seventh	Sahasrara (thousand petaled)	Top of the head	Up & down

Figure 26. Chakras from the yogic tradition.

has evolved or is evolving in and out of chakras as well. Some chakras will be found at the traditional locations, but are classified as minor, not major chakras. Verify this for yourself with detection.

Table 1 (page 62-63) gives an idea of the organs that correspond to each chakra and the diseases that can be treated by each chakra. Table 2 (page 64) gives some of the minor chakras that I use all the time in treatments and find very useful for treating specific diseases. The chakras listed as traditional (see figure 26, page 66) do not necessarily correspond to the Western system presented here for healing. It is best to approach these as two different systems, one evolving to fit modern man, and the other a traditional view compiled in and relevant for the time and place it was developed.

To actually find a real yogi to explain the traditional view is very difficult, from my experience. The real yogis that I have met have told me not to waste my time on systems and methodology, rather to go directly to the source of all phenomena and realize that which is always and has always been present. It requires no method or practice. It does, however, require a completely determined, focused, and unwavering mind to turn back on itself. Table 3 (page 65) gives a summary of the traditional yogic system of chakras. For a good honest explanation of the traditional system, *The Serpent Power* is the most accurate account I have seen.

This is a good time to address the issue of what it means to justify an experience simply because it is "our experience." The mind has unlimited powers of imagination. This is a very real power, capable of creating an entire universe. For a full explanation of how the mind is capable of doing this, study the *Yoga Vasistha*. The best translation is by Swami Venkatesanada, issued under the title *The Supreme Yoga*.[3]

What does this subject have to do with chakras? It requires a mind (thinking) to have an "experience." The mind is capable of imagining anything, so it can also create any internal

---

[3] Swami Venkatesananda, *Yoga Vasistha: The Supreme Yoga* (Shivanandanagar, Uttar Pradesh, India: Divine Life Society, 1991).

or external "experience" of the chakras. Therefore, it is necessary to verify your experiences with the yogic scriptures, or still better with a teacher who is qualified. Watch out for the imagination and how it can influence your perception of the chakras.

The spiritual and healing teachers that I have had have all advised me to do nothing directly with the chakras. They explained that the chakras will naturally develop as our inner understanding deepens. Of course, I didn't listen to my teachers; I spent many months doing different exercises on the chakras—with crystals, with prana, developing psychic powers, and using many methods to "open" the chakras. I can say from my own experience that more damage than good is done by doing these exercises. Interfering with nature just causes imbalances in the body. Beware! Many "experiences" occurred during those exercises. Unfortunately, none of those experiences changed my life in any lasting way; they proved interesting but worthless in terms of real change.

This is the basic difference between the perception of yoga and the perception of the West. Experiences are not given any value in yoga; at best they are a distraction. Here in the West we are addicted to experience. Our culture craves any kind of experience, the stronger the better. This is not only detrimental to our health, but also to meditation and energetic medicine.

CHAKRAS AT THE PSYCHOLOGICAL LEVEL

To begin to understand the psychological dimension of the chakras, it is necessary to step outside of the mind or mental conceptions. If this basic step is not taken first, it is impossible to view mind and its psychological make-up objectively.

It is obvious: to look at something, we must be outside of it—if we are not, then our view will be limited. For a clear view, distance is necessary. A good analogy might be that the best way to view the ocean is from a mountain; or better yet an airplane, and not from the water itself. To look at the psychological aspects of the mind from within the mind is to look at the ocean from under the water. The view is limited, and if we open our mouths to speak, water will enter.

This is why the tradition of yoga is so great. It was founded by enlightened sages who could and did view the mental process as separate. Their perceptions of psychology are far more penetrating than those that have developed in the West. The major difference is that yoga was the original holistic approach to body/emotion/mind/spirit. Its view of psychology was never split from the physical or the spiritual. Each mental or psychological perception was accompanied by an understanding that there is also a transcendental factor. This transcendental factor is that which jumps out of intellectual concepts and into our formless nature.

Each chakra has two aspects to it; they are opposite to each other. There are many levels, each level having both aspects. Until we pass out of duality, or polarity, everything operates as opposites. Chakras are no exception. Any system that fails to offer the "positive" and "negative" influences is only half true. Here I do not intend "positive" or "negative" in the sense of "good" or "bad," but rather in the sense of electrical polarity; yin and yang. Both must exist together.

Each chakra has what is called a transcendental quality, beyond its psychological aspects. When we transcend the two opposing orientations, there is an altogether different phenomenon. The tendency of modern Western psychology is to imagine that there is nothing beyond the constructed mental reality, including consciousness, the unconscious, and the collective unconscious. The ancient scriptures of yoga do not deny the existence of psychological problems, however the emphasis is on transcending rather than analyzing the cause, effect, and result of our psychological problems. My experience is that when I transcend the psychological polarities, I am truly healthy.

Just as there is only one human body, with layers that vibrate at different frequencies, so the chakras have an affinity with the layers of the body that match their vibrational frequency. The psychological aspects of the chakras that correspond to the appropriate body layer by vibration are listed below.

FIRST CHAKRA

ENDOCRINE GLANDS—ADRENALS, TESTICLES.

Description— Source of vitality for the physical body, physical strength and well-being. Controls the genital area, legs, base of the spine, skin, bones, and blood. Supplies prana to the upper chakras. First chakra is the center of survival and procreation, and vibrates with the physical body. The polarity of this chakra is the incoming/outgoing of the breath. To transcend this chakra is to go beyond animal survival instincts.

Malfunction— Obesity, hemorrhoids, constipation, bladder infections, cancer, leukemia, blood disease, back problems, leg problems, physical disorders of the genitals, and psychological disorders.

Psychological Aspects— First orientation is toward material needs of home, money, food, and possessions. Survival and reproduction are the focus of attention in life. Has difficulty in giving and receiving in relationships; lust is the aspect of sex in this center. Psychologically stable, relates well with the body and concrete reality.

Second orientation is usually disconnected from the material world, concrete reality and the physical body. Tends to be a dreamer and can be psychologically unstable. Also has difficulty in giving and receiving in relationships.

SECOND CHAKRA

ENDOCRINE GLANDS—OVARIES AND TESTICLES.

Description— Source of the etheric body. Controls the sexual organs and the elimination system. Storage area of prana. Second chakra is the center of influences, feelings, sexuality, and love/hate. Its polarity is of attraction and repulsion, like and dislike. Desires arise from this liking and disliking. To transcend this chakra is to move beyond preferences, or likes and dislikes.

Malfunction— Impotency, frigidity, sexual difficulties or sexual diseases of psychological origin, kidney problems, back problems, and intestinal disorders.

Psychological Aspects— First orientation is towards sexual relations, relationships, and personal power. Feeling is the primary focus in life. A need to be loved and to love; relationships are a major factor. If overdeveloped, the tendency is to be extroverted.

Second orientation is directed away from personal relationships, usually resulting in problems related to sexuality and physical contact. A lack of personal strength; the tendency is to introverted.

THIRD CHAKRA

ENDOCRINE GLANDS—ADRENALS, SPLEEN, PANCREAS.

Description—Source of the astral body, the center of individualized consciousness, or ego. Controls the digestion and the absorption of food in the body. Also controls almost all of our internal organs below the diaphragm, and the temperature of the body. Third chakra is a storehouse for prana. Its polarity is power: powerful or powerless (sometimes called "personal magnetism"). When we transcend this polarity the result is peace.

Malfunction— Diabetes, hypoglycemia, ulcers, liver diseases, stomach problems, digestive troubles, low vitality, nervous tensions, and fevers.

Psychological Aspects— First orientation is a strong personality and usually a strong, vital physical body. A "magnetic" presence, can control situations for personal benefit. Competition, domination of others, personal success, and possessiveness in relationships are some signs of this center. Represses emotions. Usually the person is under tension or is very tense and tends to be extroverted.

Second orientation is toward avoidance of competition, desire to remain unnoticed or invisible, and insecurity in life and relationships. Emotional. Usually under tension, and tends to be introverted.

FOURTH CHAKRA

ENDOCRINE GLANDS—THYMUS.

Description— Source of the mental body, the center of love. This chakra controls the circulatory and respiratory systems. Its polarity is thought coming in and thought going out of consciousness. When we transcend this polarity, we transcend mind or thought, and the result is divine love.

Malfunction— Asthma, high blood pressure, heart disease, lung disease, and childhood diseases.

Psychological Aspects— First orientation is toward loving others. Generally a giving, sharing person, feeling and emotional, yet relaxed and able to express these qualities easily. Love is directed toward people, animals, and nature, but perhaps not to oneself. Relates well to people, but may not be grounded in physical reality; orientation is toward acceptance of others.

Second orientation is a lack of love for oneself, and being closed off from others. Can relate, but without the quality of love. Usually stored pain from childhood prevents love from flowing in or out, as it activates that pain. Can also be cold and inhuman.

FIFTH CHAKRA
ENDOCRINE GLANDS—THYROID, PARATHYROID.

Description— Source of the spiritual body, controls the throat area and the vocal cords. The fifth chakra is the center of expression and purification. Its polarity is life and death; to transcend life and death is to know the immortal or spiritual self, yet still as an individualized consciousness.

Malfunction— Sore throats, colds, neck problems, and disorders of the thyroid.

Psychological Aspects— First orientation is the ability to express ideas and to communicate clearly with others. Spontaneous responses to people and situations, a general lack of fear.

Second orientation is inability to express well. Holding emotions in this center results in being, "all choked up." Fear of exposing oneself, lack of spontaneity. Personality is unable to expand in work or life, and unable to create new ideas. Generally fearful.

SIXTH CHAKRA
ENDOCRINE GLANDS—PINEAL, PITUITARY.

Description— Source of the cosmic body, controls the eyes, nose, lower brain, the endocrine system, and the nervous system. The sixth chakra is the center of intelligence or subtle mind. It has the ability to pierce the veil of illusion that is the source of our problems. This center has the polarity of creation and destruction; to transcend this is to be the witnessing consciousness.

Malfunction— Blindness, headaches, colds, cancer, allergies, and disorders of the endocrine system.

Psychological Aspects— First orientation is sharp mind, intelligence, and discrimination.

Second orientation is dull mind, slow to respond, lack of discrimination, and possibly psychotic tendencies or psychological disorders.

SEVENTH CHAKRA
ENDOCRINE GLANDS—PITUITARY, PINEAL

Description— Source of the seventh body, controls the brain and all the other chakras. The seventh chakra is the center of pure consciousness, the unconditioned source of the manifest and the unmanifest. The polarity is being or non-being; to transcend this is to be the beyond, Supreme Knowledge.

Malfunction— Brain disease, psychological disorders, and disorders of the endocrine system.

Psychological Aspects— None

We as humans are constantly changing phenomena. We are movement. Prana is that movement. The chakras, like the rest of our body, are animated by that prana. This is life in the form with which we are most familiar. It is obvious that we are a blend of all these chakras at all times and that they cannot be separated from each other.

We can speak only of "degrees" of imbalance with the chakras. It is only in extreme pathological and psychotic cases or death that a chakra is "closed." Because we are in constant motion, it is impossible to fit human phenomena into a rigid, fixed system, unless that system is also in constant change. Even this explanation of the chakras itself is in constant change— used only as a guideline to point in a certain direction.

What is that direction? It is the transcending of the psychological aspects of the personality. To have a personality is normal; who doesn't have one? To be troubled by your personality is the disease. Every person is a manifestation of that pure Source, God or Consciousness. To constantly remind yourself and others of this is, in my opinion, how best to utilize the chakras.

This is what Sri Bhagavan Ramana Maharshi has to say about meditating and utilizing the chakras:

> *Question—"Since Sri Bhagavan says that the Self may function at any of the centers or chakras while its seat is in the Heart, is it not possible that by the practice of intense concentration or dhyana (meditation) between the eyebrows this center may become the seat of the Self?" Answer—"Any consideration about the seat of the Self is theoretical if you fix your attention on a place in the body. You consider yourself as the subject, the seer, and the place where you fix your attention becomes the object seen. This is merely mental imagery. When, on the contrary, you see the seer himself, you merge in the Self and you become one with it. That is the Heart."*[4]

The heart of which Ramana speaks is not the fourth chakra or the heart chakra; it is another name for the Self or God or Love.

---

[4] Sri Ramana Maharshi, *Be As You Are*, ed. David Godman (New Delhi, India: Penguin Books India, 1992), p. 115.

CHAPTER 11

PRANA IN THE SECOND BODY

The Prana, with which we are all familiar, coupled with the five organs of action, forms the vital sheath. Permeating the material sheath it engages itself in all activities as if it were living.

—Vivekacudamani (v. 165)

The second body or the etheric body is called the pranayama–kosa, body of prana or the vital sheath in yoga. This is the body that collects and distributes the prana for all of the bodies. It is in this body that the nadis and chakras function. All diseases manifest first in this body before the physical body. Therefore working at this level can also be preventive health-care.

DESCRIPTION OF THE SECOND BODY

The second body collects and distributes prana throughout the bodies by use of the chakras and the nadis, which "live" in the vibration of the etheric level. The chakras, through the nadis, distribute prana to every cell in the physical body. The etheric body is the "electric wiring" of all the bodies. All movement or action is made possible by this body. It also animates the five senses. We perceive the world through the senses. In yoga, the etheric body is also called the "sense body."[1] Many people have tried to find correspondences between the nadis and the nervous system. It seems that there is a relation, but they are two separate systems. One operates on the physical level and the other on the etheric level. The nadis supply the nerves, along with the rest of the body, with prana. It is through the nerves that the five senses send their impressions to the brain. The first chakra, at the pubic area (front) and the base of the spine (back), is the center where all the nadis begin.[2]

As stated in the description of the psychological aspects of the second chakra, which corresponds to the second body in this system, feeling is the primary theme of this body. The polarity of this body is attraction and repulsion. This manifests through the five senses and through the "sixth sense"—the "knowing" that we often have about something, or psychic intuition.[3] Simply stated, this is the body of feeling. We either like or dislike things, people, and places due to the influences on this body.

The etheric body extends beyond the physical body some two to four inches. The primary flow of energy is usually from the feet to the head, or from the head to the feet. The etheric body is easily seen by the average person. It is the most dense of the subtle bodies and usually has an electric-blue color.

The etheric body has two layers to it: the first about three-eighths to three-quarters of an inch from the physical body, the second varying from one and one-half to four inches, depending on the vitality of the person. Kirlian photography works on the first layer of the etheric body. Many acupuncturists are now using Kirlian photography to diagnose their patients because of its extreme accuracy. The etheric body is the blueprint for the health of our body; by healing the etheric body, the physical body will also be healed.

---

[1] *Talks with Sri Ramana Maharshi*, ed. Swami Ramanananda Saraswati (Tiruvannamlai, India: Sri Ramanasramam, 1984), p. 234.

[2] Read Sir John Woodroffe, *The Serpent Power* (Madras, India: Ganesh & Co., 1989) pp. 109–115, for a full explanation of the nadis and this correspondence to the nervous system.

[3] For a very complete explanation of the manifestations of prana in the seven bodies read Bhagwan Shree Rajneesh, *Meditation: The Art of Ecstasy* (New York: HarperCollins, 1978).

APPLICATION OF PRANA IN THE SECOND BODY

The first task in dealing with the second body is the detection of its outer limit. In order to work on the second body, it is helpful to locate the limit, although it is not absolutely necessary. This is done with detection. If at first the limit is not felt, do not worry; the prana will still work.

In order to start detection, first activate your hands. When your hands are sensitized, then you can begin detection. Do not overcharge yourself with prana at this point; just activate your hands. If your hands are overcharged with prana, it can interfere with detection, as the hands will not be in a receptive mode, but rather in an active mode.

To accurately detect the second body, start about eight inches above the physical body, then slowly move your hand down until a layer of energy is felt. Usually the easiest place to feel the second body is over the second chakra, as it is generally a very strong center of prana (see figure 27, page 78).

The second body is not the same thickness everywhere on the physical body. For example, on the arms and legs, we find the layer slightly thinner; around the sides of the body, it is thinner than in the front and back of the body, and it is often much thicker around the head area. If we think logically about this, it makes perfect sense. The areas of the body where our vitality is the strongest are the areas where the second body is the thickest. When using detection, proceed slowly and carefully to verify the different thicknesses around the body.

Once the second body has been located, then detection or scanning begins for the discovery of any imbalances. Remember, detection or scanning is done with a neutral mind. At this point, we are just locating any disturbances or imbalances in the energetic body.

Check each chakra, starting from the first, moving up to the seventh, and then proceeding to all the main organs of the body. Follow the instructions in chapter five for detecting, remembering the location of disturbances. If your hands should

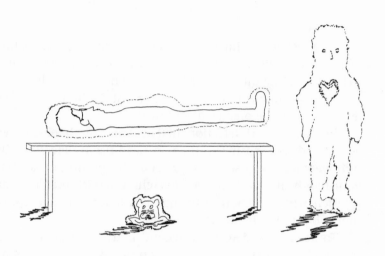

Figure 27. The etheric body.

Figure 28. Cleansing the etheric body.

become too hot, shake them several times or wash them with cool water if the excessive heat is not removed by shaking. Having hands that are too hot will interfere with accurate detection; the heat is simply an accumulation of prana. I generally have to shake my hands of excess prana several times during detection.

After detection has been completed, charge yourself with prana—four or five breathing cycles should be enough. Now commence with general cleansing. Review chapter six for a description of how to do general cleansing. Remember to have an etheric waste disposal unit (such as a bowl of salt water) to receive the etheric matter that is cleansed off the person; or for advanced students, burn all waste with the attention.

By giving prana during cleansing, more etheric matter is carried away. Remember to "sweep" the person on the exhalation and rest on the inhalation. This prevents any etheric matter from entering in your system. Three or four times is sufficient; be sure to cleanse the front, sides, and, if a back problem exists, the back. General cleansing can be done effectively when the person is standing, if this is preferable. Start on one side of the body, do a sweeping motion three times; move to the back, do a sweeping motion three times; repeat on the other side. Now end with the front of the body, with three sweeping motions (see figure 28, page 78). Start with the hands over the top of the head, continue down the body to the feet, and end with a flick of the hands to throw off the etheric matter.

After cleansing is completed, go back to the areas where some disturbance was felt and do detection again. This is called "reverifying" your work. This is the reason why there is no fixed system in pranic healing, because you constantly "reverify" your work. After cleansing or energizing, always reverify if the body feels calm and even.

There are now two choices: either you can do local cleansing on a specific area or you can energize a specific area. Normally, both local cleansing and energizing are done together in various combinations. Energizing has the effect of breaking up congested etheric matter, but cleansing is necessary to remove the matter once it has been "broken up." This process is repeated over and over to harmonize the second body. Each time

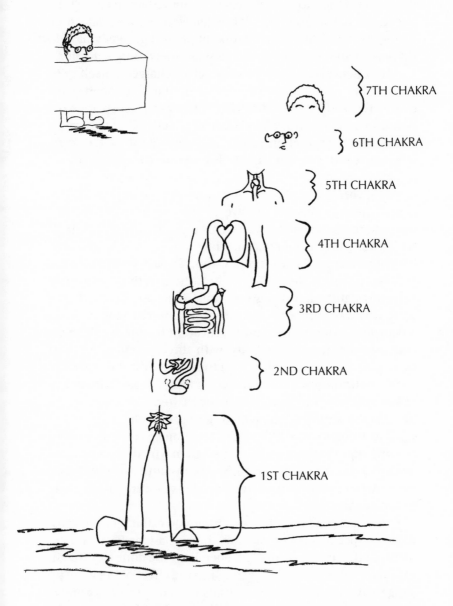

7TH CHAKRA

6TH CHAKRA

5TH CHAKRA

4TH CHAKRA

3RD CHAKRA

2ND CHAKRA

1ST CHAKRA

Figure 29. Major chakras and their corresponding organs and body parts.

you energize or cleanse, it is necessary to reverify the state of the second body. For a review of how to energize, read chapter seven. Remember to breathe during the treatment as it will keep you rooted in your own body, charge you with extra prana, and increase the amount of prana being sent by a factor of three.

The same method that we learned for the first (physical) body can also be used on the etheric body, that is, the opening and charging of the primary and secondary circuits of prana. Any combination of working etherically and physically can be done at this time. If the problem is muscular or tension-related, it is very effective to work physically after general cleansing.

At the level of the second body, we can work with the chakras. This is the level of physical health, because, as stated before, diseases manifest first in the etheric body; by healing the second body, the first body is also healed. The chakras, at this level, are related to the physical functions of the body. Repeat the three steps over the body as needed, cleansing and energizing any affected places or organs. Reverify the second body to confirm that a normal healthy feeling pervades evenly throughout before stopping.

A word about working on the major organs of the body. First, any organ that is delicate or physically fragile will likewise be fragile etherically. Use care when charging; do not overcharge delicate organs. This is virtually impossible if you are present and attentive, if the prana is carrying the quality of love, and if you reverify after every four to five breathing cycles.

If in any place on the body an excess of prana is felt, simply do local cleansing until it is normalized. The organs should be treated in a fashion similar to the chakras. Follow the explanation for cleansing and charging the chakras for the organs as well. The chakra that controls the organ in question should always be cleansed and charged first, as it is the "pumping station" of prana for all the organs in its region. Use Table 1 (page 62) to find the controlling chakra for the organ in question.

If the Table is not available, simply divide the body into seven regions, with each region having one of the major chakras in it (see figure 29, page 80). It is simple and logical to locate the controlling chakra for all the major organs.

Figure 30. Closing the etheric body.

Now the second body must be closed. The prana that has been sent to revitalize it must be sealed inside, or it will leak out after twenty-four to forty-eight hours. Closing or stabilizing the prana is the last step of working on the second body. If this is not done, then the person will most probably experience a loss of vitality, or even a recurrence of the illness.

This is done by focusing the attention and the prana to stay with the person. I use another method: I "ask" the prana to stay with the person. I accompany the "asking" with a movement of my hands, starting from the top of the head and moving down to the bottom of the feet (see figure 30, page 82). At the same time that I ask the prana to stay, I give prana, much the same as cleansing, only the prana will carry the quality of stabilizing or staying rather than of cleansing.

At the end of every treatment, no matter how long or short, I silently thank the person for the opportunity to work with them. If it were not for this person, I would not have had an outlet for the creative aspect of the prana. Doing this work brings great joy to me, therefore I am grateful. It also provides money for my daily living; for this too, I am grateful.

Now you must cleanse yourself. Wash your hands and then do the self-cleansing exercise. Look ahead to the section on treatment (page 86) for a step by step review of a treatment.

CHAKRAS IN THE SECOND BODY

Before working with chakras, it is important to know two things: they are extremely sensitive regions of the body and must be approached with infinite respect; and any work done by a therapist or healer can only be of temporary help. Lasting, permanent change must always be generated from within by a change in life style, diet, and/or doing meditation, prayer, or self-inquiry.

To work with the chakras, the same three steps described in chapters five, six, and seven are used: detection, cleansing, and energizing. During detection, the chakras are checked for any kind of disturbances; after general cleansing, the chakras can be addressed.

Reverify any of the chakras that were disturbed before cleansing; always start with the lowest chakra and proceed to the highest. It is wise always to check the legs before starting on the chakras. A large amount of prana is received from the feet and legs, moves up to the first chakra, then is pumped by the first chakra up to the other chakras. Therefore, a depleted first chakra can often be caused by a blockage in the legs. If the first chakra is depleted, the other chakras will also suffer.

A chakra will either need to be cleansed, energized, or both. Because a chakra can be rotating in both directions (see page 59), I find it the least aggressive method to open and cleanse a chakra without using the spinning motion advocated by some systems.

By pointing the hand, fingers down, over the chakra at the etheric level (see figure 31, page 84), then opening the fingers like an umbrella while giving prana, the chakra is opened (see figure 32, page 84). This is repeated several times as needed. Then either cleansing or energizing can be accomplished without affecting the normal rotation.

Usually this whole process is repeated several times: detection, opening, cleansing or charging; detection, opening, cleansing, etc. The determining factor in choosing either cleansing or

Figure 31. Inserting a hand into a chakra.

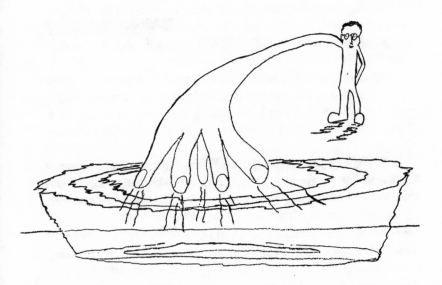

Figure 32. Opening a chakra.

charging (energizing) is the strength and feeling of the energy radiating from the chakra.

Always cleanse first; it is after cleansing that energizing may be used to stabilize the chakra. When a good healthy feeling of energy is felt in the chakra, *stop*. Overworking an area is a common mistake. Usually three or four times, at the maximum, is enough to stabilize the chakra. If it has not stabilized, stop, go on to another area, and recheck after about five minutes. Never force any work, anywhere on the body. Force, or the intention to heal, is aggressive, and therefore not loving and not a part of pranic healing.

The best way to end the individual work on the chakras is to connect them energetically. This is done by simply holding a hand over the first and the seventh chakras at the same time, and waiting until a current or a connection of energy is felt. This will align all of the chakras so that one will not have a greater charge than another, and will make certain that no blockage exists between any of the centers.

If for some reason no connection is felt, start with the first and second chakras, then the first and third, then the first and fourth, up to the first and seventh. If this does not solve the problem, reverify with detection all the areas between the first and seventh chakras. Ordinarily, thirty to sixty seconds is enough to connect the first and seventh chakras. Check the top of the head for an even flow of prana leaving, as with the physical body.

Another simple technique that I use very often is to balance the left and right brain by the use of the minor chakras just in front of the ears. This is done by lightly touching, or remaining one inch away from, the minor chakras in front of both ears and giving prana. A current of prana is formed between the hands, thereby equalizing the amount of prana in each half of the brain. It is very important that you be calm and relaxed for this technique; whatever state you are in will be passed immediately to the patient. I usually take one minute to visualize that I am floating in a womb-like space, safe, secure, resting, and peaceful. Stay like this; give prana for four or five breathing cycles before ending.

Remember, before stopping the treatment, close the second body by focusing the attention or by "asking" the prana to stay, and give thanks for the opportunity to give the treatment. For a quick reference, all the steps are listed below for working on the second body.

TREATMENT OF THE SECOND BODY

Start by having the person lie down comfortably, facing the ceiling, hands resting at their sides. Inquire about any difficulties or pains they may be having in their body.

FRONT OF THE BODY

1. Charge yourself with prana; three or four breathing cycles are enough.

2. Relax the person and create space in the neck and head by using the neck release method; stay for three to four minutes.

3. Move to the bottom of the feet; verify the direction that the prana is flowing in the legs and feet by detecting the foot chakras.

4. Press the solar plexus point on the feet for three to four minutes; give prana. Shake off extra prana from the hands when finished.

5. Start detection from the feet going slowly up to the head. Take as much time as necessary, be thorough, and remember the places that need to be checked after cleansing.

6. Now charge yourself with prana—five to six breathing cycles are sufficient—remember to breathe throughout the treatment, constantly maintaining a surplus of prana. Do not, however, overcharge.

7. Do general cleansing, starting with your hands over the top of your head and exhaling as you "sweep" the etheric body of all unwanted matter. Throw all etheric waste into a disposal unit. Repeat three to four times.

8. Go back to any questionable areas, starting at the feet and moving toward the head, reverifying with detection any area that needs work.

9. Work on any area that needs it by cleansing locally and energizing; always reverify after energizing or cleansing.

10. Work on the physical body if needed; use any of the steps from Steps in a Treatment of the Physical Body (see page 43). Or give a massage if needed.

11. Check each chakra again, starting from the first and moving upward to the seventh. Stop and work on any center that requires treatment. Open and cleanse any chakra that you work on; do not just energize.

12. When all the chakras feel alright, connect them energetically by making a circuit between the first and the seventh. Check the top of the head to verify a good flow of prana. Repeat if necessary.

13. End with the neck release, or by balancing the left and right brains, or both.

14. Close the etheric body by asking the prana to stay in the body of the person. Pass over the major chakras to insure that they are closed as well.

15. Thank the person silently.

16. Wash your arms and hands from the albows down with cool water and soap.

17. Do the exercise for self–cleansing.

18. Wake up the person; advise them of the three-day period of adjustment and request that they drink several quarts of water for a few days to eliminate toxins.

BACK OF THE BODY

1. Follow steps one through four for the front of the body.

2. Have the person roll over onto their stomach.

3. Do detection on the back of the body, checking the legs and spine carefully.

4. Do general cleansing.

5. Reverify the spine and any other areas; cleanse and charge locally; reverify.

6. Follow steps four through seven from the section on the back of the physical body (page 49).

7. Repeat the same steps, but this time only on the etheric body.

8. Check the top of the head for a good flow of prana leaving the crown. If you are not satisfied, repeat steps six and seven.

9. Close the back of the etheric body; have the person roll over again to the starting position.

10. Do the neck release, and then give prana to the shoulders to relax the muscles.

11. Work on the front of the body if needed.

12. Follow steps fourteen through eighteen for the front of the body.

For serious diseases, always have the person consult a qualified doctor. Pranic healing is not a replacement for doctors, but rather a supplement.

Sometimes a time lag of three days exists, during which the etheric body adjusts to the new level of prana. This may be felt in several ways by the person receiving the treatment. Common symptoms are increased fatigue or vitality, fever or increase of the illness, and possible emotional swings.

These are quite normal, as the body is adjusting to new energy patterns and new energy levels which help the body to fight off illness naturally. Generally, the longer an illness has existed, or the more complicated it is, the greater the symptoms will be. For a sprained ankle, it would be almost impossible for any reactionary symptoms to occur. On the other hand, chronic asthma, for example, may involve psychological problems and some toxins in the body, and therefore may possibly entail reactions. Should any symptoms occur, they will pass within three days. If not, consult a doctor and repeat the treatment.

CHAPTER 12

PRANA IN THE THIRD BODY

The organs of knowledge together with the mind form the mental sheath—the cause of the diversity of things such as "I" and "mine." It is powerful and endowed with the faculty of creating differences of name and form. It manifests itself as permeating the vital sheath.

—Vivekacudamani (v. 167)

The third body is also called the astral, or the emotional, body. It corresponds directly to the solar plexus region, or the third chakra in the Western system. Giving a treatment on the astral body brings us into a completely different dimension of work.

DESCRIPTION OF THE THIRD BODY

The ancient scriptures tell us that the astral body extends out to a limit of twelve finger-widths, or approximately ten inches from the tip of the nose.[1] The astral body is considered to be a part of the subtle body of traditional yoga.[2] In the tradition of yoga,

---

[1] Swami Venkatesananda, *Yoga Vasistha: The Supreme Yoga* (Shivanandanagar, Uttar Pradesh, India: Divine Life Society, 1991), p. 368.
[2] See glossary, "subtle body."

the subtle body consists of the etheric, astral, and mental bodies of the Western seven-body system. They are all in the realm of the mind or mental perception.

"The reflection of consciousness within itself is known as puryastaka," the Yoga Vasistha teaches. "Mind alone is puryastaka, though others have described it more elaborately (as composed of the five elements, the inner instrument-mind, buddhi, ego sense and citta-prana, the organs of action, the senses, ignorance, desire, and karma or action). It is also known as the linga-sarira, the subtle body."[3] The importance of this quote is that it shows that the subtle body is of the mind. According to this quote, the mind or subtle body consists of: the five elements, the reasoning process of the mind, intellect, the "I" sense, memory, the five sense organs, the five senses, ignorance, desire, and action. With this description, it becomes clear that the emotions and personality must also be included, as it requires the ego, the memory, and the intellect to perceive emotions. Emotions are of the mind. When the thought process stops, this distinction becomes clear.

The astral body can be expanded and contracted by a strong intention or emotion. As stated above, the normal limit is twelve finger-widths from the tip of the nose. This can vary according to the state of the person, but generally this is the limit.

The astral body has several layers. These layers vary somewhat according to the person; or rather, "the development" of the layers is different. Often healers confuse these layers with different bodies. I have made this mistake myself, and was corrected first by my teacher, then later by yoga scriptures like the one quoted above.

These layers correspond to different emotional memories and states. They usually lie dormant until a life-situation activates them. They can also be activated in a session of therapy, revealing different insights into a person's emotional make-up. These memories and emotions tend to stay in layers, corresponding to the different desires and actions. They are easy to find and substantiate.

---

[3] Swami Venkatesananda, *Yoga Vasistha: The Supreme Yoga*, p. 384, vi 1/31.

All the bodies are insentient, without awareness or consciousness. When the individual awareness moves to the astral body, it is called the "astral plane." The astral reality is just the same as normal, waking reality, because it is still part of the mental functioning, as is the normal waking state. It is this body that we identify with in the dream state.

In the dream state, the feeling of "I" is identified with the astral body. Movements are not restricted to physical reality and thoughts can manifest immediately. There are only minor differences between the waking and the dream states. Actually, the differences lie only in a distinction between subtle manifestation and gross manifestation. Far too much emphasis has been placed on the astral plane or dream world. It is useful and can help an individual, but it is not "higher" than or better than the physical or etheric levels of reality. They all belong to the mental projection that covers reality.[4]

In the third body, we find the energetic "impressions" of all past and present experiences. A thought is a "thing," it has a subtle existence. Nothing is ever lost in the universe. Thoughts and emotions may pass out of our mental awareness, but they are all stored energetically as "impressions." It is possible to use these impressions in psychotherapy to help people resolve psychological issues.

All past-life impressions are also stored in the third body. Most of the recent parapsychology methods work on the astral body through these impressions. In yoga, these impressions are called *vasanas* and *samskaras*.

There are two ways to work on the third body, directly or indirectly. Pranic healing works directly, while psychological therapies work indirectly. The pranic therapist can work directly on these stored energetic impressions. If the person is willing to assist in this work, the results can be dramatic. However, the person can also be unaware of the impressions dissolving during a treatment, provided there is the willingness to undergo a

---

[4] For a full explanation of the similarity between the waking and dream states read *Tripura Rahasya*, trans. Swami Ramanananda Saraswati (Tiruvannamalia, India: Sri Ramanasvamam, 1989), chapter 13.

treatment. If the person is unwilling to have a session, nothing is possible.

Emotions are thoughts. Feelings are energetic. Feelings are in the etheric body—likes and dislikes, attraction and repulsion. Energy is related to etheric phenomena. Likewise, emotions are related to thought or mental phenomena. This is why the third body is often called the emotional body. The aspect of this body is of personal or individual power. We often say that a person has a "magnetic personality" or "charisma" or "magnetism;" this is the crystallization of the individual personality or ego.

The system of energetic healing in Europe called "Magnetism" comes from this aspect of the third body. Actually, there is nothing magnetic about prana or the subtle bodies. The primordial prana is before, and therefore the cause of, all polarities.

When someone is emotionally stable it means that all the emotions are functioning naturally according to the situation and not leaving an impression in the emotional body or mind. Once experienced, they are gone. An "emotionally unstable" person is one who is traumatized later by a previous emotion or has a reoccurring emotion that does not correspond to the present situation.

My observation is that the only way to be really stable emotionally is not to identify with the mental functions or emotions. This does not mean repressing emotions or thoughts; rather it means knowing that we are the underlying source which perceives emotions and thoughts. And it does not mean that we will not continue to have thoughts and emotions. By knowing that I am not either an emotion or a thought, I will cease to create energetic impressions. When the emotions and senses function naturally, without the interference of the mind, there is peace or emotional stability. Identification with the mind or the emotions is the cause of the disease.

Disturbances in the astral body influence the etheric and the physical bodies. Diseases manifest first in the finer bodies and then move into the more dense bodies. If a disease cannot be effectively healed in the etheric body, then the astral body must be addressed. A disease that recurs when treated etherically is being re-manifested in the astral or mental bodies. Therefore they must be treated as well.

APPLICATION OF PRANA IN THE THIRD BODY

The procedure for working on the third body is the same as the procedure for working on the second body, with a few additions. Throughout all of the bodies, we will utilize the same three steps: detection, cleansing, and energizing. The subtler qualities of the human being are revealed as we move progressively into the finer bodies. To work effectively on the third body, it is helpful to have developed your hands enough to feel the subtle differences in the prana. I call these subtleties the "quality" of the prana.

Work on the third body is almost exclusively with the different qualities of the prana. Never for a moment assume that any of the bodies are static. This is particularly true of the third body. It comprises a constant fluctuation of influences, emotions, and polarities of power and powerlessness. What will often remain fairly constant is the quality of the prana in a given area or region.

This is the limitation with any fixed system, but particularly in the case of the third body, because it changes from one second to the next, just as our moods and thoughts change. This is why it is important to sense the different qualities in the third body.

What is meant by quality? The quality is what attaches to the neutral prana. Prana is energy without any quality. The quality is, for example, prana + joy = joy, or prana + anger = anger, or prana + greed = greed, or prana + happiness = happiness. In a treatment, we sense the quality of the prana and, according to the situation, we may help change that quality.

For example, I may feel a quality of "tightness" in the astral body over the throat area. The person would probably feel much better if the quality were changed to a calm, light, or open quality. The quantity of energy may be the same or it may change; that is independent of the quality that is associated with the quantity.

Also, it is not possible to change the quality of an area if the person doesn't want it to be changed. If, during your work, it doesn't change, don't worry. It isn't the right time.

Sensing the quality is not an intellectual affair. It entails sensing with the whole body. You may feel the example of tightness in your own throat; or you may just feel the tightness in your hand; or your whole body may feel tight. Remember, detection does not need the thinking process. To detect the quality, no thinking is required; in fact, it will interfere and give an incorrect interpretation, because once the mind is activated, it automatically interprets. Mind means interpretation. Detection is just feeling "what is." Never come to any conclusion; conclusions classify individuals.

CHAKRAS IN THE THIRD BODY

The nature of the chakras in the third body reflects the emotional countenance and general personality of the individual. The areas that are commonly referred to as chakras hold, in the astral body, energetic memories. These memories can be activated by giving prana directly to an area, or just by touching an area with prana.

One supposed expert in esoteric matters told me there are forty-nine major chakras, because there are seven chakras in each of the seven bodies. This is not maintained in any of the yogic scriptures, although it is possible that it may be found in some obscure doctrine. However, it is not my experience.

The more I work on the chakras in the third body, the more I reach a conclusion slightly different than the common understanding of them. The ancient scriptures of yoga refer to the location of the chakras as an area or region, not as a specific point. This accounted for differences in individuals and allowed for changes. The scriptures rarely talk specifically about the chakras in the emotional body or mental sheath, but usually refer to them as a purely energetic phenomenon in the energetic body.

If, however, the chakras are used to activate different experiential states of consciousness, as in kundalini yoga, then the situation changes. For the normal person or for the average practitioner, the chakras as energetic centers do not exist in the third body.

The chakras do exist in the second body as distribution centers of prana, and there is an energetic phenomenon in the outer bodies that corresponds to the region of the chakras in the second body. The energetic areas above the etheric chakras are not chakras as we know them; rather they are collections of energetic memories and impressions of this moment, this life, and past lives. This is not the technical definition of a chakra.

Every modern system with which I am familiar calls these energetic areas chakras. Why then do we find no reference to this in yogic scriptures? Why do we find numerous references to vasanas (latent tendencies or unconscious impressions) and samskaras (innate tendencies or conscious impressions)?[5] Why are the vasanas and samskaras said to exist in the subtle body? Why not the chakras?

The obvious conclusion is that we have not understood the scriptural description of a phenomenon that usually occurs in a certain region, namely over the chakras. For example: latent impressions of one kind will generally be found in the region of the solar plexus, or another kind may generally be found in the pubic region. These energetic areas are not chakras as normally understood; rather they are the concentrations of the latent and innate tendencies stored energetically above the etheric

---

[5] Swami Venkatesananda, *Yoga Vasistha: The Supreme Yoga*, pp. 5, 351, 361, 385, 400, 414, 416, 429, 452, 460, 486-487, 492, 502, 515, 524-525, 529, 535, 573, 580, 628, 653, 746, 748. See also Swami Hariharananda Aranya, *Yoga Philosophy of Patanjali* (Calcutta: University of Calcutta, 1981), I.5, I.40, I.50, II.12, II.15, II.24, III.18, III.49, IV.8, IV.11; and *Talks with Sri Ramana Maharshi*, ed. Swami Ramanananda Saraswati (Tiruvannamalai, India: Sri Ramanasramam, 1984), pp. 29, 82, 123-124, 280, 248-249, 351-352, 497, 576-577.

chakras. I am not saying that there are no chakras in the astral or mental bodies; there are. They are there as concentrations of latent and innate tendencies.

In yoga, they say that a person must do years of very specific meditations before a chakra becomes activated in these bodies. Chakras are not activated unless this training is done. That means that 99.9 percent of the people in the world do not have chakras in any form other than pranic distribution centers in the second body.

I am suggesting a different perspective on the chakras at the level of the astral and mental bodies: that these areas really are energetic storehouses for all impressions past, present, and future. Anyone working on the chakras at this level will have experienced the emotional memories stored there.

These latent impressions we now call the unconscious tendencies of the mind. The innate impressions are referred to as conditioning, mental attitudes, and mental habits. Modern psychotherapy and psychology are working to dissolve these energetic patterns indirectly; pranic healing works directly to dissolve the energetic tendencies, conscious and unconscious. Both systems are effective and each complements the other. Pranic healing is not antagonistic to any other system of medicine or therapy.

The real work on the third body is to dissolve these impressions. This is an extremely strong form of therapy and should be respected as such. It is impossible to force these patterns to leave or dissolve if the person is unwilling. Another way to dissolve all impressions, conscious or unconscious, is in the presence of love. Love can only descend or appear in a thought-free state; it cannot be cultivated. In Its presence true healing just occurs.

TREATMENT OF THE THIRD BODY

Start by having the person lie down comfortably, facing the ceiling, hands resting at their sides. Inquire about any difficulties or pains they may be having in their body or life.

Front of the Body

1. Charge yourself with prana; three or four breathing cycles are enough.

2. Relax the person and create space in the neck and head by using the neck release method; stay for three to four minutes.

3. Move to the bottoms of the feet, verify the direction in which the prana is flowing in the legs and feet by detecting the foot chakras.

4. Press the solar plexus point on the feet for three to four minutes; give prana. Shake off extra prana from your hands when finished.

5. Start detection of the astral body from the head, going slowly down to the feet. Usually I make several passes to cover the left side, the right side, and the middle of the body. Take as much time as necessary; be thorough, and remember the places that need to be checked after cleansing. The emphasis is on the *quality* of the prana.

6. Cleanse the third body with general cleansing; three to four times are enough. This will close any tears or rips if done correctly; remember to give prana during cleansing.

7. Detect and cleanse the second body.

8. Reverify any areas in the third body that were disturbed before general cleansing.

9. Do local cleansing and energize as needed in the third body. Work if needed on the chakras in the same manner as the etheric body. The emphasis is on the *quality* of prana.

10. Now start the treatment for the etheric body, local-cleansing and energizing as needed. It is fine to work etherically, then go back to the astral body. It is also fine to start work on a chakra at the astral level, go to the etheric level, and then to finish with the physical level, proceeding on to the next place or chakra on an astral or etheric level. You can change levels as needed after general cleansing.

11. When you are done with the chakras, connect them energetically by placing one hand over the first and another over the seventh. Wait until you feel a current flowing between them.

12. When your work is finished with the physical and the second bodies, close the third body first, then go to the second body and close it.

13. Thank the person silently, and wash your arms and hands from the elbow down with cool water and soap.

14. Do the exercise to cleanse yourself.

15. Wake up the person; advise them of the possible three-day period of adjustment to the new levels of prana and request that they drink water for several days to help eliminate toxins.

BACK OF THE BODY

Working on the back of the astral body is the same as for the back of the etheric body, only before detection of the etheric body, do detection and general cleansing astrally. Proceed as above, just remember to close the astral body first, before the etheric body.

The most important factors of the third body are the qualities of the prana, the latent impressions stored energetically, and the present impressions stored energetically. It is absolutely clear from research and practical work with my clients that the energetic patterns and centers in the astral and mental bodies are *vasanas* and *samskaras* attached to regions of the different chakras. The chakras themselves provide the energetic centers for these impressions to gather. These impressions only exist in the subtle body of yoga, or the etheric, astral, and mental bodies of the Western world. Our approach to the third body must always be reverent; this is a highly sensitive body for everyone, therefore we must proceed with care and understanding, and, if we are fortunate, with love.

CHAPTER 13

PRANA IN THE FOURTH BODY

The subtle body is produced out of the elements before their subdividing and combining with each other, it retains latent impressions and causes the soul to experience the fruits of its past actions. It is a beginningless superimposition on the soul brought on by its own ignorance.

—Vivekacudamani (v. 97)

The fourth body is the mental body in the Western system. In this chapter, we will consider how we can best utilize prana to help us psychologically. First, we must understand the nature of disease and how it manifests.

ENERGETIC PSYCHOTHERAPY

According to yoga, disease is the wrong identification of who and what we are. This is called ignorance in the scriptures of ancient yoga. For yoga, the body/mind/emotions are not who we are, rather they belong to us. We are that which has no name or form—the awareness of awareness. The disease process was described by the seer Vasistha thousands of years ago:

Ignorance gives rise to absence of self-control and one is constantly assailed by likes and dislikes and by thoughts like: "I

*have gained this, I have yet to gain that." All this intensifies
delusion; all these give rise to psychic disturbances.*

*Physical ailments are caused by ignorance and its compan-
ion total absence of mental restraint which leads to improper
eating and living habits. Other causes are untimely and ir-
regular activities, unhealthy habits, evil company, wicked
thoughts. They are also caused by the weakening of the nadis
or by their being cluttered or clogged up, thus preventing the
free flow of life-force. Lastly, they are caused by unhealthy
environment.[1]*

What Vasistha said 7000 years ago is still the truth today, because the basic cause of disease is the same. Disease is the lack
of knowledge of who we are, which gives rise to ignorance. In
yoga, disease on the physical level is due to lack of free movement of prana in the nadis. The nadis or canals of prana in the
body become clogged or congested. "If the movement of the
life-force is governed in such a way that it neither goes up or
down, there is an unceasing state of equilibrium and all diseases are overcome. Otherwise, if there is a malfunction of ordi-
nary (secondary) nadis, one is subject to minor ailments and if
the principal nadis are involved there is serious ailment."[2]

We as humans are psychosomatic phenomena. It is absolutely impossible to separate our physical body and environment from our mental and emotional states. This is why the
mental body affects the astral, etheric, and physical bodies.
Health begins with the understanding that we can and do create our own health. The first step to regaining health is the
understanding that we can change the root causes on all levels:
mental, emotional, energetic, and physical. It probably will not
be easy, but it is possible and necessary.

Let's look at this a little more closely. Perhaps I have created
this disease because of some psychological problem or mental

---

[1] Swami Venkatesananda, *Yoga Vasistha: The Supreme Yoga* (Shivanandanagar,
Uttar Pradesh, India: Divine Life Society, 1991), p. 441, section 6.1,
chapter 81.
[2] Swami Venkatesananda, *Yoga Vasistha: The Supreme Yoga*, p. 441, section 6.1, chapter 81.

habit, but how will that knowledge help me now? The idea is that acceptance and responsibility for our disease start the moment we understand that mental habits are its root cause, not before. Healing starts with the firm decision to change whatever is necessary to regain health. If this decision is not made, then the root of the illness will remain untouched. It will be possible to treat only the effect or the manifestation of the illness; this is what allopathic medicine does. Psychotherapy tries to uncover the roots of the problem, but does not treat the physical body.

The best approach to this situation is a holistic one, or one that takes into account all the aspects of a person's life, and deals with it as a complete unit. But if the fundamental step of accepting responsibility is not taken, healing will be superficial at best.

How to take responsibility? Look for the roots of the illness by searching for:

1. Destructive mental habits,
2. Destructive physical habits,
3. Conditioning from parents, school, society, country.

Understanding is the key. Another way to look at this is by inquiring into our mental patterns. They change without effort by the very act of seeing them.

When looked at with a completely objective attitude, mental patterns cease their relationship to the conditioning. The problem lies in our identifying with our learned personality, and having a relationship with it. The ego or mind lives and grows by this false relationship. It is the ego or mind which gives rise to our illness, mental and physical. Understanding means recognizing that relationship is false. We exist before all conditioning, mental patterns, energetic memories, and ideas. Understanding is seeing—direct perception of what is.

From the standpoint of yoga, only those who are ready to accept life as it is now, and inquire into the nature of their selves, are truly ready for health. The definition of health is "soundness of body and mind." True health must include mental and emotional well-being, as well as physical health. We as individuals must start with a willingness to change whatever is needed to cure ourselves. Then miracles can happen, regardless of the medical system being employed. Too often in today's world, we want to place the responsibility on our doctors, governments, parents, spouses and just about anybody else that is available. When we make the decision, however, true healing is possible on all levels.

The next step to good health is to control the prana. It must be obvious by now that the binding factor in good health is the prana. As explained in the first chapter, prana and intelligence arise together. Emotions need a mind to perceive them and a body to feel and express them; they come into existence after mind/prana. Therefore, when the prana is controlled and regulated in the body, the whole being is harmonized. Conversely, when mind is controlled, the prana is harmonized.

THE DIRECT APPROACH OF PRANA

When prana is directed to the fourth body, the thinking process is directly affected, which in turn affects the other three bodies below. The energetic impressions that we discussed in chapter twelve also hold true in the fourth (mental) body. The difference is that they are of a purely mental nature. In other words, the third body can have emotions, past lives, and energetic memories. The mental body holds the impressions of all of our thoughts. The longer a thought is kept, the stronger the impression becomes. "Whatever one constantly contemplates, whatever constantly occupies one's mind and to whatever one is devoted with all his life, that he knows to be real and obvious. . .whatever the mind loves most it becomes that."[3]

An example: holding a negative thought for ten years against someone without telling them of your negative feelings. The continuous thought to which this gives life is an energetic pat-

---

[3] Swami Venkatesananda, *Yoga Vasistha: The Supreme Yoga*, p. 684, section 6.2, chapter 175.

tern that will manifest a disorder in our body eventually. Usually the disorder comes as a heart attack, tumor, ulcer, or cancer. Negative thoughts kill us eventually. The facts are obvious. If there is any doubt about habitually suppressed emotions or negative thought patterns affecting our health, one should read books available on these subjects. There has been much good research done on this subject. I have experienced this directly with my own body.

Yoga knows of the energetic impressions and their relationship to prana. In fact, it is the prana that gives the power for recording all impressions in the four bodies. "All the 24 hours, this vital breath, or vital force, through various perceptions, is recording the pictures of all your experiences and memorizes whatever is relevant. Can you do that with your intellect?"[4]

When the direct relationship of mind to health is realized, work on the fourth body has already begun. As a practitioner of energetic medicine, it is possible to assist in the dissipation of thought patterns. The first requirement is the patient's willingness to have a treatment. The second requirement is a willingness to change ideas and thoughts. Strong mental ideas, or resistance, will block the prana given by the practitioner. It is possible to force stronger prana on the person with mind, but the karma or backlash on the healer will be heavy indeed. This is violence, not true healing. Although many times healers who work like this get very good results, eventually they will have to pay the price. And usually, after some time, the person will again manifest the same or another illness because the root cause has not been changed.

It is often thought that the patient needs to assist in the dissolution of thoughts and energetic patterns. This is helpful, but not necessary. In fact, some of the best results I have witnessed have happened in a completely nonverbal atmosphere where the patient is not actively assisting the process. My own preference is to work in this manner. The moment words are brought into a treatment, mind is activated. Energetic thought patterns are dissolved more easily in a quiet mind. Many times

---

[4] Sri Nisargadatta Maharaj, *Prior To Consciousness,* ed. Jean Dunn, (Durham, NC: Acorn Press, 1985) p. 29.

I have witnessed the totally calm, quiet face of a patient change after a treatment, as the thinking process starts to activate the habits of tension and worry.

It is immediately obvious if a person has allowed the energetic thought patterns to dissolve for good, or if they recreate them as soon as possible. My own results in this nonverbal energetic psychotherapy are 50 percent effective for complete change, and approximately 80 percent effective for partial change. Twenty percent of patients I am not able to help at all. The reasons for this are many: I may have no energetic affinity with the person; I may be having an off day; the person may want to change, but certain ideas and concepts prevent the prana from entering; the person may unconsciously derive love and attention from the illness; or the person may have a preconceived idea that I am going to help, or not help, them.

By a complete change or a partial change, I mean direct relief of the current problem troubling the patient. Of course, we as humans are constantly changing and growing; what was a problem last year is not relevant this year. Final and ultimate healing can only be done by ourselves for ourselves. In yoga, this is called liberation—liberation from concepts and habits of mind that bind us to limited ideas of the body/mind/emotion phenomenon.

What is the proper technique for working on the fourth body? Fundamentally, it is the same as that for the etheric and the astral bodies, but with a slight difference. Energetic thought patterns dissolve when there are no thoughts moving in the mind of the practitioner. And many times when there is no movement of thought in the mind, something else arises.

HEALING WITH LOVE

When movement of thought stops, sometimes another power descends or arises to spontaneously guide the treatment. Love is the word we usually associate with this divine force which, uncalled for, arises to replace the healer, the healed, and the healing. This Love is not an emotion or a feeling; it can not be induced; it can not be called; it may or may not come; it may or may not heal the illness. But certainly all are humbled and touched to the core of their being by this unnameable power.

This Love is not possible to know, to understand, or to grasp. It is the true healing force, for it is the very source itself. Prana and mind arise from this Love. When mind and prana cease to move, they slowly drop back to the place of their origin. This source is who we are—the core of the creation.

What is usually called love in healing systems, is subtle mind. True love cannot be *known*, much less called or manipulated. Love is not energy or prana. Many healing systems and healers mistake the wonderful feeling, the emotional bliss, the experience of giving, for love. It is not. This is also true for virtually all spiritual seekers as well. Everyone mistakes the experience for the source of the experience. People have spent thousands of years trying to explain the unexplainable. All my healing teachers have misunderstood this distinction.

From the unmanifest source, the entire creation arises; first, individualized consciousness, then prana and mind, then the body and the five senses. By arresting the prana or the mind, we fall into subtle mind or individualized consciousness. This is what is mistaken for love; it is not, because we still exist as an individual to recognize and experience the moment. It is very beautiful, very silent, seductive, and blissful. And it is not yet the source of creation.

True health exists at the source, even though our bodies may be ill and sick. If a perfect body is desired, master the prana in the body. If something else, something unknown, is pulling you, then follow the prana and the mind to its source. This has been the beginning of true health for me.

CHAPTER 14

QUESTIONS ANSWERED

I am neither formless nor with form. My nature is neither pure nor impure. I am neither beautiful nor ugly. I am that Supreme Reality which shines in Its own nature.

—Avadhuta Gita III.45

There were several personal questions that kept troubling me over the years as I worked with energetic medicine. I sincerely looked for answers to these questions. Perhaps they have been answered in other publications without my knowledge. If not, these questions and answers are presented here in an effort to share what I have found, not because "I know," but rather to pass on the information that I have received in hopes that, together, many of us can remedy the pervading misunderstandings which surround energetic medicine, regardless of the tradition.

Question: What is Prana?
Answer: Prana is the active principle of all existence, often called the life force. Intelligence is the other principle of existence. Together these two principles are responsible for all manifestation, seen and unseen. It is not possible for either of these two principals to exist without the other; they are like two sides of a coin. They both arise from a substratum that has various names, depending on the tradition: God, Consciousness, Love, Self,

Brahma or Source. When prana or intelligence cease their activity, they automatically fall back to their source with the other accompanying principle. "It is only because of forgetfulness of truth that the confusion arises that the unreal is real. By the purification of the life-force (prana) and by the knowledge of that which is beyond this prana or life-force, one gains knowledge of all that is to be known concerning the activities of the mind as well as the basis for the succession of births."[1]

Question: Is love different from prana?
Answer: Yes. Love is another name for the substratum from which prana and intelligence arise. When prana ceases to move, it falls back into Love; at that moment Love itself takes over the action. There may or may not be action; that is the responsibility of Love. Love chooses the way. "That from which all thoughts of embodied beings issue forth is called the Heart. All description of it are only mental concepts." [2] "Love is not different from the Self. Love of an object is of an inferior order and cannot endure. Whereas the Self is Love, in other words God is Love."[3]

Question: Is there a transfer of karma during a healing treatment? Am I interfering with this person's karma?
Answer: Yes. There is a transfer of karma during a treatment. All disease occurs for a reason. Commonly this reason is called "fate," or, if there is an understanding that we go through many lives before realizing our source, it is called karma. Karma means that which is the result of action. It is neither good nor bad in itself; it just reflects the action.

When I asked Sri Poonjaji this question of karma, his response, as I remember, was: "Yes, if you remove a disease, where

[1] Swami Venkatesananda, *Yoga Vasistha: The Supreme Yoga* (Shivanandanagar, Uttar Pradesh, India: Divine Life Society, 1991), p. 168, section 4, chapter 18.
[2] Ganapathi Muni, *Sri Raman Gita* (Tiruvannamalai, India: Sri Ramanasramam, 1992), p. 25.
[3] *Talks with Sri Ramana Maharshi* (Tiruvannamalai, India: Sri Ramanasramam, 1984), p. 401.

does it go? It goes on YOU; nothing disappears in the universe until YOU disappear." He went on to say that, as long as there is an intention to heal, there is a transfer of karma. The difficulty with this is that, as long as we are thinking, there is some intention; and if we try not to think, that is also an intention. Clearly, the answer is to work without a mental process, therefore without intention. Then there is no transfer of karma, because there is no individual "I" who is doing anything; the responsibility rests with the greater "I." When there is no mind, there is no prana moving; that means both have fallen into their source. Now it is up to that source to deal with the karma or nonkarma. "How to get released from karma? See whose karma it is. You will find you are not the doer. Then you will be free. . . . The karma which takes place without effort, i.e., involuntary action, is not binding."[4]

Question: Is it possible for disease to enter my body during a treatment? If so, how do I prevent that from happening?
Answer: Yes. A thought is enough to receive a disease. To prevent that, do not think during a treatment; have no intention. It is very important to wash your arms and hands from the elbow down and to do the self-cleansing exercise given in chapter six. This helps to greatly reduce the risk.

Question: What is noneffort in healing? Does it mean becoming a "channel"?
Answer: To think requires effort. Nonthinking is noneffort. Prana is in motion to allow thinking, because it is the principle of motion. Effort requires movement of thought; thought requires movement. To not think is what is meant by "noneffort." No intention or effort can stop thinking. "The wise ones declare that the mind is caused by the movement of prana; and hence by the restraint of the prana, the mind becomes quiescent."[5]

---

[4] Ganapathi Muni, *Sri Raman Gita*, p. 108.
[5] Swami Venkatesananda, *Yoga Vasistha: The Supreme Yoga*, p. 313, section 5, chapter 78.

Question: Is my ego increasing by healing others?
Answer: Yes. Anything that is done with an intention or pre-conceived idea is increasing or reinforcing the individual "I," or ego. This is known as separation. In the absence of thought, where is the separation and with whom? It requires a mind to think for a separation to exist. The individual "I" arises before mind/prana. If the mind/prana are still, the individual "I" will fall back to its source. Constant thinking and action only reinforce the individual "I." To have the idea that "I am a healer" is to hold a concept that creates separation and reinforces the ego. No thought or concept of a healer is the alternative.

Question: What gives me the right to heal others?
Answer: If people come to you for help, help them without any intention. If no one comes for help, then where is the question? Why is there a mystique surrounding healing and healthcare? It is natural to help a sick person in your family. Is not the human race a family? It is absolutely correct to charge a reasonable fee for a healing treatment. Fortunately or unfortunately, money is necessary to live in our society. If you can afford to give treatments without charging money, try doing it. My experience is that, unless people pay you, they rarely benefit due to the psychological aspects of value. Part of not taking responsibility is paying someone else to take it for you.

Question: Are psychic powers really a hindrance to true healing?
Answer: Real healing takes place when we return to that source from which we arose. No tensions or diseases exist in the source of existence. By returning there, the purpose of existing here as we commonly understand it is fulfilled. This is true healing. Our bodies may still be in pain; we may die; but all that now happens is from the knowledge of the whole, not from the limited understanding of the ego or "I."

If a person wants to be a great healer, he/she can easily develop psychic powers in a few years, but the price to be paid is heavy. It must be clear by now that to have any intention to "be" a healer or to "heal" a person incurs a heavy personal toll in terms of returning to your source.

First, who is it that wants to have psychic powers? It requires a mind to have this idea; mind means thinking; thinking reinforces the ego, and thereby the idea of "I," "me," and "mine"; that equals separation from your real "I." Second, when we say "I have healed..." or "I see their aura...," who is it who has healed or seen? It must be the ego.   Third, when we say "I am just a channel for...," that may well be, but who is saying this? A channel may have been opened during the treatment, but watch out for afterward! The ego loves to act egoless.

The only exception to this is if, without effort, these powers come to you unsought. Then it is your responsibility to use or not use them, as the situation dictates. "Occult powers are in the realm of the mind only....Occult powers will not bring happiness. Moreover why are they for? To make others praise one's ego! God, Self, is the highest power and most worth seeking. That which results in Peace is the highest occult power." [6]

NO HEALER; NO INTENTIONS

As I understood more about healing and working with prana, it became apparent that I needed to lose my thinking process while giving treatments. This is not really what it seems to indicate. On the one hand, I am writing this book to explain how to use a certain method of healing, and on the other hand, I am now saying "Don't think, don't have any intentions, and don't do anything."

It is really very simple: "No healer; no intention" is the result of the method of pranic healing. It will happen naturally, as any skill or art flowers into a creation. So working with prana will lead you to its source if you are attentive. At that source

---

[6] *Conscious Immortality,* ed. Paul Brunton (Tiruvannamalai, India: Sri Ramanasramam, 1984), p. 174.

there is no healer, no patient, and no healing. It is beyond all concepts, dualities, or differences that are inherent in the mind. Just as we need all our concentration to learn how to drive a car, so too we need our concentration to learn the techniques of pranic healing.

It should be understood clearly that to simply respond to the situation of someone coming to us for a remedy does not constitute "doing" or "ego" or "mind." Healing is a natural function, just as illness is a natural result of making incorrect choices of diet and life style. Simply respond to the situation, go through the three steps outlined in this book, and treat the afflicted areas as needed.

If the technique works for that person, it works. If not, then it is not your responsibility. Do not assume responsibility for another person's illness. Each person has their own karma and life style that is their own personal responsibility. To have any idea about being able to heal another person is an intention.

While you are learning the art of energetic medicine, mistakes will occur. This is natural. It is the responsibility of the teacher to point out the possible traps to anyone who wishes to pursue energetic medicine. To teach can be difficult. The compulsion to share a beautiful natural method of healing is also a good opportunity for the ego to assert itself. It is often necessary for me to stop, distance myself from the situation, and reevaluate what is happening. I suggest the same for anyone wishing to pursue energetic medicine professionally.

NO METHOD; NO PRECONCEIVED IDEAS

This has been mentioned several times throughout this book. I consider it to be one of the most important aspects in pranic healing and the health profession in general. Nothing feels worse than being thrown into a classification by another person. When that person is someone that we have gone to for help, it is even worse.

My personal experience in therapy is that, every time I was classified in any way whatsoever, I automatically withdrew to some extent. On the other hand, whenever I was approached as an individual, I responded with sincerity and honesty. These reactions are normal for the average person. Every human being is unique and wants to be recognized as such. To have any system or preconceived idea automatically classifies individuals.

Again and again we come back to the importance of not activating our minds during a treatment. When the mind is not activated, no system, intention, or idea is possible. While it may take some practice for us to slow down or stop the mind, the Jnana Yogis say that it takes no time.

They say the person with a very sharp intelligence can be directed to see the source of the mind or the prana. This indeed does not require time or practice. But for an average person like myself, help is required. I needed the guidance of a Master to be able to stop the ever-active movement of thoughts, even after ten years of meditation. When in fact it did happen, no effort or time was required, because the happening is out of time itself. Time is confined to the realm of mental concepts or mind.

This book is a simple effort to explain a method of energetic medicine that is so natural to human beings that it has existed as long as mankind has lived on this planet. I was lucky to have the right person to help me realize the thought-free state, the natural state. This, however, is by no means a qualification to help others achieve it or even explain it clearly.

It is possible to be in a thought–free state while working. This has happened naturally to me over the years; the result of my life search. Most of all, the meeting with my Master is directly responsible for my realizing this freedom to work and abide in a thought-free state. This brought the missing link that I had searched for all my life. Anyone who sincerely pursues pranic healing will also arrive at this, the Great Void, the Source of all, as it is the natural destiny of human beings.

CHAPTER 15

PRANIC TREATMENTS

The food articles which maintain the equilibrium of bodily tissues and help in eliminating the disturbance of their equilibrium are to be regarded as wholesome; otherwise they are unwholesome.

—Caraka Samhita XXV.33

By far the best pranic treatment is to eat correctly. By changing your diet and life style, it is possible to live happily and healthfully your whole life. As a teenager and as a young man, I very often suffered from nasal allergies and colds. I took medication for several years. After several years of eating a vegetarian diet and a four month long herbal treatment, these problems ceased. Over a period of time, diet can change virtually all problems, because food is one of our main sources of prana.

DIET

The medical system of Ayurveda stresses the fact that medicine is usually a last resort in regaining health. Bad habits result in a loss of health. Because Ayurveda and yoga come from the same tradition, their methods are complementary. By following the daily regimes and dietary plans laid out in Ayurveda, disease can be prevented. Ayurveda, also understands prana and how it functions in the body through diet, exercise, and life style.

Personally, I eat a vegetarian diet and follow the energetics, food combinations, timings, and principles of Ayurveda. There are many advantages to this way of eating and living. It is not the purpose of this book to outline a complete dietary regime, but rather to recommend what is complementary to pranic healing. Ayurvedic dietary and life style regimes are the best for people working with prana to follow.

The most important factor in any diet is to eat food with abundant prana. Fresh foods that are in a natural state have the most prana. Avoid processed foods of any kind. If you eat a diet with meat, avoid commercial meats; buy direct from farmers or from a natural food store.

Food is a main source of prana; if attention is given to diet many small and troublesome illnesses can be relieved over a period of time. The body is a complex machine; it takes time for the body to expel toxins and pollutants that have accumulated in the intestines and body tissues. Please avoid drastic diets of any kind; they usually do more damage than good.

Ayurveda points out that fasting or drastic changes in the diet disturb the balance of the three humors. Your individual constitution must also allow fasting. There are several very good books on this subject and how to structure your diet, among them: *Ayurvedic Healing*, by Dr. David Frawley, and *Ayurveda, The Science of Self-Healing*, by Dr. Vasant Lad (see Recommended Reading, page 141, for complete publishing information for these books).

If you are sensitive to your body, you know what to eat. Follow the body; it has a wisdom of its own and knows what it needs. Follow the mind (desires) and trouble will result.

In this chapter treatments are given for simple, everyday illness. They are accompanied by diagrams showing which chakras to cleanse and charge. Unless stated, these treatments can be given locally with the person lying down or sitting in a chair. These treatments are most effective in the early stages of illness, but even if the problem is chronic, regular treatments will eventually cure most problems. Always follow your doctor's advice for serious diseases or chronic problems. My experience is that 80 percent of diseases can be helped or cured with pranic healing. Charge yourself with five to six breathing cycles before giving any of these treatments.

COMMON COLD

This treatment is very effective if it can be given in the first twelve hours of catching a cold. If it is later than twenty-four hours, then repeat this treatment every six to twelve hours until the cold leaves. It is no longer necessary to suffer from colds; as soon as the first symptoms are felt, give your partner or child a treatment, and within six to twelve hours the cold will be completely gone. Try it and see!

1. Start by cleansing the neck and head, from the shoulders up to the top of the head, four or five times.
2. After local cleansing, scan the front, sides, and back of the head. If you find any congestion, cleanse the area until it feels normal.
3. Charge the sixth chakra for four breathing cycles; cleanse two or three times and charge again.
4. Charge the two minor chakras just in front of the ears for three breathing cycles (see figure 33, page 118).
5. Charge the two minor chakras below the nostrils for three breathing cycles (see figure 33).
6. Charge the two minor chakras under the eyebrows and at the root of the nose for three breathing cycles (see figure 33).
7. Scan the complete head area again; cleanse again if necessary, then repeat the last three steps.
8. Finish by charging the sixth chakra again for three cycles.

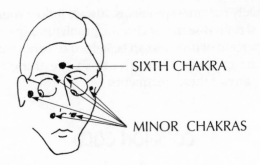

Figure 33. Chakra locations for a cold treatment.

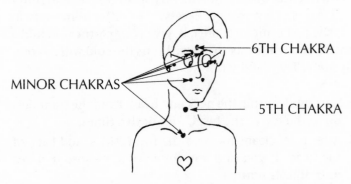

Figure 34. Chakra locations for a cold with bronchitis and a cough.

Figure 35. Charging the sixth chakra—front and back.

BRONCHITIS AND COLDS WITH A COUGH

1. Give the treatment for a cold; after finishing with the sixth chakra, cleanse and charge the fifth chakra for four breathing cycles (see figure 34).
2. Charge the minor chakra at the base of the neck, just between the two collar bones, for four breathing cycles (see figure 34).
3. Scan the lungs and cleanse if necessary; usually only the top of the lungs are affected, which area is controlled by the minor chakra at the collar bone. If the middle or lower lungs are congested, cleanse and then charge the fourth chakra for four breathing cycles (see figure 34).
4. Rescan the throat area and cleanse if necessary; repeat charging the minor chakra.
5. Finish by charging the fifth chakra for three cycles.

NOTE: The minor chakra at the base of the neck, between the collar bones, is, in yoga, the Visuddha chakra. It is the most important chakra for the top of the lungs, the throat area, and coughs. I usually charge it two or three times, with cleansing as needed. Repeat this treatment every six to twelve hours until the symptoms leave.

HEADACHES

1. Scan the head area; if possible, find any concentration of energy.
2. Cleanse the head, from the shoulders up to the top of the head, especially any area of intense concentration.
3. Charge the sixth chakra for five to six cycles with one hand on the front and the other on the back simultaneously (see figure 35).

4. Directly charge any concentration of energy for five to six cycles.
5. Charge the two minor chakras in front of the ears for four breathing cycles (see figure 35, page 118).
6. Cleanse the entire head again.
7. Repeat the complete treatment until the pain is gone or reduced. Often, it may take an hour or two for the pain to leave completely.

NOTE: For a migraine or chronic headache, a complete treatment is necessary because the cause may be from a malfunctioning organ, such as the liver or the intestines.

FEVERS AND FLU

Fevers and flu require a complete treatment. The person can be lying down in bed or in a comfortable position. Usually the fever or flu will increase after the treatment before getting better. Repeat this treatment every six to twelve hours until full recovery is obtained.

1. Scan the area of the second and third chakras; usually a fever is centered in the third, and the flu in the second and third, chakras.
2. Do general cleansing for the entire body.
3. Rescan the trunk of the body; do local cleansing where needed.
4. Energize the body through the feet for six cycles.
5. Charge the first chakra for six cycles.
6. Charge the second chakra for five to six cycles.
7. Charge the third chakra for five to six cycles.
8. Cleanse all of these chakras again and charge; scan between each cleansing and charging. Repeat cleansing and charging three to four times, or until the chakras feel normal.

9. Give a treatment for a cold or headache if either symptom is present.
10. Scan the whole body again; cleanse locally if needed.
11. Close the etheric body.

ACHES AND PAINS IN THE NECK AND SHOULDERS

All muscular aches and pains in the body are healed more effectively by touching the physical body after cleansing the etheric body. The technique called neck release will, if done correctly, heal 80 percentof all neck problems.

1. Have the person lie down comfortably.
2. Start with the neck release; stay for eight to ten breathing cycles.
3. Do a head release, the same technique as the neck release, only applied to the base of the skull.
4. Cleanse the shoulders and head area etherically.
5. Charge the shoulders, fingers under the shoulders (see figure 21, page 48).
6. Charge the shoulders, fingers over the shoulders (see figure 21).
7. Place one hand under the neck behind the fifth chakra; give prana for four breathing cycles. With the other hand, cleanse the front of the fifth chakra simultaneously.
8. Charge the front of the fifth chakra for three cycles.
9. Put both hands under the edges of the shoulder blades, next to the spine; give prana for five breathing cycles. Slowly move your hands to the neck; do the neck release for five cycles.
10. Detect the top of the head to check if the prana is moving out easily. Neck and shoulder tension is caused by the prana being congested. If the prana is moving out of the crown easily, it means that the nadis are open.
11. Repeat every three to four days until the problem disappears.

ACHES AND PAINS IN THE BACK

Start by checking the feet and legs for blocks or congestion of prana. A majority of back problems are the result of congested prana in the legs, which in turn deprives the first chakra of prana. A good healthy back is dependent on a vital first and second chakra. If the first chakra is deprived of its normal supply, back problems can result.

1. Follow the steps given in chapter 8 (page 49) for treating the back of the body.
2. After following steps one through seven use the optional technique given on page 51.
3. Place the hands directly on the painful area; give prana for four to five breathing cycles.
4. Finish with steps eight and nine for the back of the body (see page 49).
5. Repeat every three to four days until the problem disappears.

ASTHMA

Asthma is an inflammation of the bronchial tubes and the lungs. Most doctors agree that psychological causes are the initial reason for the manifestation of this illness. However, once manifested in the physical body, it must be treated as a physical illness. I have had very good results treating asthma by cleansing the etheric body.

1. Have the person either sit, stand, or lie down.
2. Detect the lungs, throat, and head; also check the third chakra etherically.
3. Scan the astral body to check for any disturbances. If any are there, do general cleansing astrally.

4. Do general cleansing on the etheric body.

5. Check the lung area again; do local cleansing if necessary.

6. Charge the third, fourth, and fifth chakras for three breathing cycles.

7. Do local cleansing again over the third, fourth, and fifth chakras.

8. Redetect (scan) the lungs and throat area; repeat charging and cleansing if needed.

9. Close the astral and etheric bodies.

10. Repeat every three to four days until the problem disappears.

ECZEMA AND SKIN PROBLEMS

Eczema is generally a disease that manifests from a change in life. In these periods of change, emotions that appear can, if not expressed, produce eczema. Another major cause of all skin disorders is the exit of internal toxins. When the body becomes overloaded with excessive toxins, they naturally find a way to leave the body. The primary paths for expelling toxins are through the intestines, through the urinary system, through the sinuses and lungs, and through the skin. Cleansing the etheric body is very important in treating skin problems.

1. Start with a general treatment. Check the astral body for any possible emotional disturbances.

2. The emphasis is on cleansing. After the general treatment of the astral and etheric bodies, check the legs for a good circuit of prana; open and charge if necessary.

3. Charge the first chakra, as it controls the health of the physical body.

4. Check the third chakra for depletion, cleanse and charge if necessary.

5. Check the fourth chakra for depletion; cleanse and charge if necessary.

6. Cleanse all affected areas of the skin locally.

7. Charge all affected areas directly for three to four breathing cycles; cleanse and charge again.

8. Connect the first and seventh chakras, making sure that all the other chakras are open and the flow of energy is moving out through the head.

9. Recheck the astral body and cleanse if needed.

10. Close the bodies.

11. Repeat every three to four days as needed.

DIGESTIVE PROBLEMS

Problems in the digestive system are a simple case of eating the wrong food and, as mentioned before, an accumulation of toxins that need to exit the body. The primary factor for good health in the digestive system is the quality of the food that is put through the system. This is not a book on diet, but it is obvious that if a chronic problem exists, the diet must be changed. Problems can occur in the digestive system if one or two of the organs are sluggish in their job. By energizing the controlling chakras (two and three) and the organs that are undernourished, the system can be revitalized and balanced. This, however, will only be a temporary cure if the root of the problem is not addressed.

A word of warning: the digestive system has a built-in default system; that means that, if one organ is not doing its job, another organ or several organs will have to work harder to make up for the sick organ. In detection, we usually feel the overactivated organs. Look for the root problem, possibly a nonfunctioning organ. If the overactivated organs are not treated, they will also malfunction over a period of time due to excessive work. Cleanse and charge the underactivated organs and cleanse and charge the overactivated ones. In this way, the system can be balanced. And remember to change the diet!

1. Check the astral body for disturbances; often our emotions are reflected in the digestive system. Cleanse and charge as needed.
2. Now move to general cleansing of the etheric body.
3. Do detection to find the under-and overactivated organs.
4. Do local cleansing as needed.
5. Cleanse and charge the second chakra for four to five breathing cycles.
6. Cleanse and charge the third chakra for four to five breathing cycles.
7. Work with the individual organs as needed, cleansing/charging the weakened ones and cleansing/charging those overworked.
8. Go back to the second and third chakras to cleanse and charge again.
9. Close the bodies.

It is common that, during the next elimination, the stool may be loose and foul smelling. This is a good sign that toxins are leaving the body. If constipation continues for more than thirty–six hours, give another treatment. If constipation still continues another twenty-four hours, consult your doctor. It is very important to drink more water than usual after a treatment of the digestive system—at least two quarts per day for two days. Another very helpful thing for the intestines is to take a natural bacteria, called lactobacillus acidophilus, that helps digestion. Repeat this treatment twice a week until the system is stabilized.

CLOSING NOTES

These treatments are very effective if done correctly. Here are some things to remember:

1. Always charge yourself before a treatment.

2. Always cleanse yourself and your room after a treatment.

3. Time is not a factor in a treatment; if done correctly, it can be done in ten to twenty minutes or it can take an hour, depending on the situation.

4. Proceed slowly with children and the elderly; better to give many soft treatments than to shock the body with too much energy in one treatment.

5. These are guidelines; you will find each situation is different. Don't hesitate to experiment; you cannot harm another person with prana given from a Heart with no intention.

Major diseases can be treated with pranic healing. The purpose of this book is to provide simple, effective remedies for the common diseases. For a serious disease, apply the same methods as for common ailments. It is advisable to work with a teacher of energetic medicine and a medical doctor until enough experience is accumulated. To treat a member of the family that has any of the major diseases, follow the instructions for the second body in chapter eleven. A serious disease may require daily treatments, because the incoming prana must always be stronger than the disease. This is especially true for cancer and AIDS. In this respect, a member of the family suffering from a life threatening disease is at an advantage by having easy access to numerous treatments.

It is also my experience that any long-term illness, serious or otherwise, is best treated with herbs, tinctures, or homeopathic medicines as well as pranic treatments. According to Ayurvedic medicine, the longer a disease remains untreated, the deeper it penetrates into the tissues of the body. A long-term (four to six months) herbal treatment is necessary to drive the disease from that deeper level. This combination is a much more effective way to work than with either prana or herbs alone.

It is always fine to give prana sessions when a person is under allopathic treatments. The problem with allopathic drugs is that they are toxic by nature, due to their synthetic manufacture. Only natural medicines have prana in them. Science has not learned how to create drugs that keep or have the most important ingredient: prana/intelligence.

As Dr. Deepak Chopra has pointed out in *Quantum Healing*, manufactured drugs do not have the intelligence to locate the correct destination on a cellular level.[1] Yoga teaches us that prana and intelligence are inseparable. One must use live medicines (i.e. medicines with prana) in order to add the factor of intelligence and eliminate the factor of toxins.

---

[1] Dr. Deepak Chopra, *Quantum Healing: Exploring the Frontiers of Body, Mind, Medicine* (New York: Bantam, 1990), pp. 42-43.

CHAPTER 16

MEDITATIONS AND EXERCISES

Truly, Brahman is identical with the individual soul. It pervades equally all living beings and all immovable things. Being the selfsame Brahman, O mind, why do you weep?

—Avadhuta Gita v.17

Here are a few exercises and meditations that I have found to be useful in pranic healing. Most of these exercises can be done anywhere, at any time, unknown to others, all of which makes them even more useful. These are the basic exercises that, if mastered, will greatly accelerate your ability to heal with prana.

PRANIC BREATHING

Pranic breathing, or complete breathing, uses the full capacity of the lungs, thereby giving us greater quantities of prana to utilize for ourselves, for others, or for meditations. The heart meditation uses the complete breath to send prana out through the heart chakra and hands.

1. Place your hands on the lower abdomen, just below the navel.
2. Inhale a breath with prana through the nose into the lower abdomen; your hands should move slightly outward, as the diaphragm is pushing the organs in the abdominal region down and slightly outward.
3. The lower abdomen is now full of air; continue to breathe in an upward motion to the upper chest.
4. Stop for a second or two when the upper chest is full of breath.
5. Exhale slowly from the chest, out through the nose.
6. Stop for several seconds with empty lungs before inhaling a new breath.
7. Repeat this cycle as necessary. This constitutes one breathing cycle.

EXERCISES TO SENSITIZE THE HANDS AND FINGERS

Move your hands apart to a distance of eighteen inches, with the palms facing each other, then slowly move your hands together (see figure 5, page 18). This should be done for ten minutes at a time. It takes several minutes, at first, for the prana to build up between the hands. Keep them together until a heat or an electric sensation is felt between them, then slowly move them apart. Repeat this exercise over and over for at least ten minutes a day, for three to four months.

This not only activates the minor chakra in the hands; it also develops the sensitivity to the etheric and astral bodies. This exercise can be facilitated by first pressing the hand chakra directly with the fingers for two or three minutes.

The fingers can be sensitized in the same manner, the tips of the fingers almost touching, fingers straight. Wait for a sensation in the fingertips; slowly move the hands apart to about eighteen inches, then slowly return to the starting position,

keeping the tips of the fingers facing each other. Repeat for five
to ten minutes each day, for three to four months (see figure
36, page 132). Sensitizing the fingers is important for working
in tight areas and pinpointing the exact place of an illness. It
usually takes a little longer for the fingers to be sensitized than
the hands. Don't lose patience! Keep going. Once the hands
and the fingers become sensitized, the sensitivity never leaves.

HEART MEDITATION

This meditation opens the circuits from the second chakra up
to the fourth chakra, and then from the fourth chakra out
through the arms, to the hands, and beyond. These are all the
circuits used in transmitting prana, so I recommend doing this
exercise for five to ten minutes each day. Do not do this exercise for more than ten minutes a day. It is very strong, and a
teacher should be present to watch the progress if it is done for
longer than ten minutes a day.

This exercise will also heal any illness related to the second,
third, and fourth chakras over a period of time. Any chronic
problems in the shoulders and arms will be helped or cured by
this technique as well. For simple illness, this method will give
immediate results; for more complicated problems, give yourself at least three months. This exercise affects the first, second,
third, and fourth bodies, clearing old energetic impressions out
of the subtle bodies.

Although this looks the same as pranic breathing, it is not.
With this meditation you give the energy out; in pranic breathing, you collect the prana for yourself.

1. Place your hands on the lower abdomen, just below the
   navel.
2. Inhale a breath with prana into the lower abdomen; your
   hands should move slightly outward, as the diaphragm
   is pushing the organs in the abdominal region down and
   slightly outward.

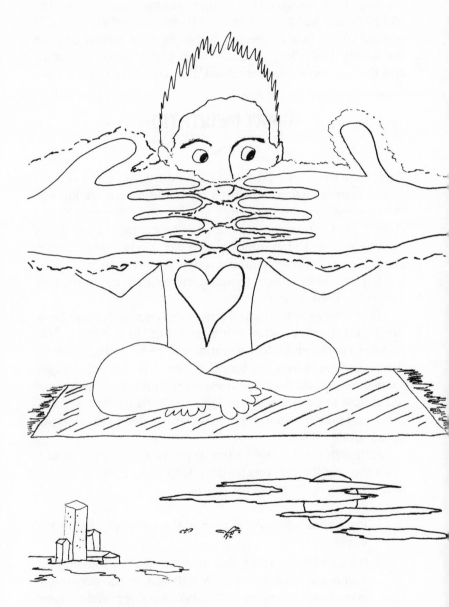

Figure 36. Sensitizing the fingers.

3. The lower abdomen is now full of air; continue to breathe in an upward motion to the heart area.

4. Stop for a second or two when the heart area is full of breath.

5. Exhale slowly from the heart, out through the arms and hands; the exhalation is through the mouth.

6. During the exhalation, move your hands and arms away from the chest in a horizontal motion. Imagine the prana carrying love out to the whole universe.

7. Stop for a second or two, then repeat for five to ten minutes.

Follow the movement of the breath with your hands; starting at the lower abdomen, rise to the heart, then from the heart move the hands out in a horizontal motion and down to the lower abdomen (see figure 37, page 134). As the hands follow the breath, so too the prana will follow the breath. On the inward breath imagine, the prana carrying fresh vitality to your body; on the outward breath, imagine the prana carrying love to the whole universe.

SELF-HEALING

One very important aspect of personal health is physical exercise. If we are healing others, it is even more important. I often don't make the time to exercise, and I usually end up paying for it in some way or another. Long walks or a daily regime of hatha yoga, tai chi, dance, etc. are some of the best forms of preventative medicine. I prefer a daily regime of hatha yoga, as it fits well with Ayurveda and pranic healing. Hatha yoga knows how to strengthen and balance the prana through physical exercise. A half-hour a day is enough to help maintain your health.

The most effective way to heal yourself is to first do the pranic breathing for ten cycles. This charges the entire body with prana and gives a good base from which to work. In addition to the normal pranic breathing cycle, imagine fresh, clean,

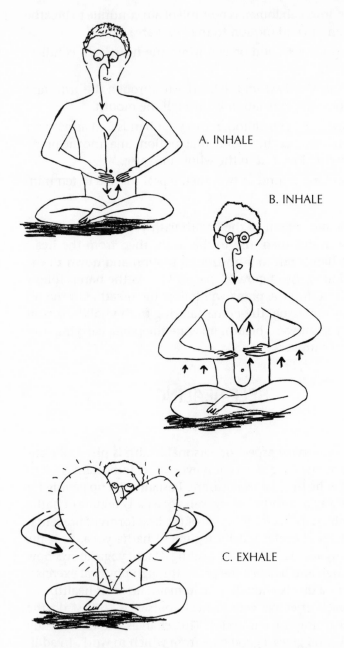

A. INHALE

B. INHALE

C. EXHALE

Figure 37. Heart meditation.

healthy prana entering your body on the inhalation. On the exhalation, imagine the pain or disease leaving your body. Colors can be used; white on the inhalation and dark brown or dark gray on the exhalation.

All self-healing should be accompanied by a dietary change. This is why the Ayurvedic system is so useful. First, it is adjusted to the individual constitution of a person and second, it teaches that many physical ailments are caused by toxins in the gastro-intestinal tract. It is necessary to reduce, or preferably eliminate, these toxins before rebuilding your body. If this is not done first, we just end up rebuilding the toxins that caused the illness. The pranic healing methods will reinforce these toxins if they are not eliminated first, or at the same time.

After ten breathing cycles, move the attention to the afflicted area. Find the major chakra that controls the area or the organ that is ill. Now do the breathing cycle directly in and out of the chakra. This charges and cleanses the major chakra that controls the afflicted area. Do this for five to ten breathing cycles or until the pain is gone.

For general afflictions, such as eczema, first do general pranic breathing, then charge the controlling chakra, in this case the first chakra, front and back (see Table 1, page 62). Now do the breathing cycle directly in and out of the skin. Imagine the prana entering directly through the skin and taking out any diseased matter as it leaves. This is called "direct breathing," and can be used on any part of the body. I recommend using the previous two steps first, as I find the combination more effective.

A completely different, but very effective, method is to imagine the diseased organ or broken bone (for example), being rebuilt and restructured by the prana. This method requires mental visualization; for those of you who find this easy, it is a good way to heal.

A broken bone or sprain can be healed in one-third of the normal time if this method is employed for ten minutes morning and night. Just imagine the prana as tiny little workers with new materials fixing up the diseased part. The new material is the fresh prana. This should be accompanied by the knowledge that the prana is coming in on the in-breath and going on the

out-breath, carrying away diseased or old matter. As these workers add new prana to the affected part they remove the old
materials and send it out of the body with the out-breath. Set
up a miniature worksite inside your body and see the results.
Too simple to be true? Perhaps, but it works very well.

> *Where is activity, where is inactivity; where is liberation or*
> *bondage for me who am ever immutable, indivisible and*
> *established in the Self?*[1]

---

[1] *Astavakva Samhita*, trans. Swami Nityaswarupananda (Calcutta:
Advaita Ashrama, 1990), p. 194.

GLOSSARY

allopathy: Western medicine, modern medicine.

ashram: Place devoted to spiritual development.

astral body: Third body in the western system, also called the emotional body.

attention: Be present; act of attending to something; different than thinking.

Ayurveda: The oldest medical system in the world, a real holistic approach developed by the same people who formed the systems of yoga; the part of the Vedas dealing with the health of the body.

causal body: The third body in the system of yoga; said to be the cause for the individual reincarnating.

chi: Chinese word for prana.

consciousness: As used in this book, the substratum or source of all manifestation.

chakra: An intersection of the nadis; a distribution center of prana; a place where energetic impressions collect; wheel. With yoga methods, they can be used as spiritual references.

cosmic body: Sixth body in the western system; also called the body of pure intelligence.

cleansing: Sweeping; second step in treating a patient.

detection: Scanning; first step in diagnosis of a patient.

ego: Personalized consciousness; I am; arises from the union of the first two principles, cosmic prana and pure intelligence.

energetic impressions: In sanskrit there are two kinds: *vasanas* and *samskaras*; these are latent, unconscious, or stored impressions and current mental impressions; these impressions are stored in the subtle body of yoga or the etheric, astral and mental bodies of the western system; yoga says that these impressions are what incarnate in another life, because they are not allowed to surface in consciousness; these impressions tend to collect around the areas of the chakras.

energizing: Third step in treating a patient; two methods, attention and pranic breathing.

enquiry: Method to find out where thoughts, prana arise; question: "Who am I?" (see books of Ramana Maharishi and H.W.L. Poonjaji).

etheric body: Second body in the western system, also called the vital body or vital sheath.

five sheaths: In yoga they connect the three bodies; they are the material, vital, mental, intellectual and blissful sheaths.

gross body: The first body in the system of yoga.

guru: Literally, a dispeller of ignorance; master; one who knows the substratum or source of all being; master of oneself.

holistic healing: A total approach to health including body/ mind/ emotions.

"I": In current non-dual teachings, it means the first concept of individuality that arises out of the unmanifest source. Prana and intelligence arise out of this concept of "I." Ramana Maharishi calls this concept "the I thought," or the first cause of ignorance.

intelligence: First principle arising from the substratum.

intention: One's purpose for doing something; object; aim; requires an idea or direction; doing.

Jnana Yoga: The yoga of knowledge or direct path; the supreme yoga.

ki: Japanese word for prana.

mental body: Fourth body in the western system.

mind: Thoughts moving, giving the illusion of continuity.

nadi: The canal which carries prana in the etheric body.

no-mind: Nonmovement of thought; complete awareness, not to be confused with the absolute; the individual may still exist at this point; it may take many times of being merged in no-mind before the individual dissolves into the divine.

physical body: First body in the western system.

prana: *Pra* (before), *ana* (breath); the vital force; ki; chi; second principle; arises from the substratum with the first principle, intelligence; together they create the individualized consciousness. There are five major pranas in the human body: prana, apana, samana, udana, and vyana. They arise from the cosmic prana, or the second principle.

pranayama: A method of breath control used to regulate the mind, the breath, the prana, and thereby the physical and mental health; should only be done with a qualified teacher.

quality: The attribute attached to the prana or body.

samskaras: Innate energetic impressions (see energetic impressions).

seventh body: Last body in the western system; no name or description is possible.

spiritual body: Fifth body in the western system; also called the intellectual body.

substratum: In this book, equal to the Absolute, Consciousness, God, Love, Brahma, Atman, Self or Source.

subtle body: The second body in the system of yoga. NOTE: In the tradition of yoga, the material sheath is within the gross body; the vital sheath covers the gross body; the mental sheath is within the subtle body; the intellectual sheath covers the subtle body; and the blissful sheath is covering the causal body. The second (etheric), third (astral), and fourth (mental) bodies of the seven-body system match the second (vital) and third (mental) sheaths and the subtle body of the yoga system, or the realm of mind. The fifth body corresponds to the fourth sheath (spiritual or intellectual) and the sixth body to the fifth sheath (pure intelligence) (see figure 2, page 10). The seventh body is another name for consciousness itself, having neither name nor form; it is said to be existence, consciousness, bliss (*sat-chit-anand*). It is interesting to note that the second body (subtle body) of yoga, and the vital and the mental sheaths are all considered to function as a unit.

tantra: A path that totally accepts all aspects of the physical world, believing that all things lead to the divine; total acceptance; often confused as being limited to sex, it is a total approach.

vasanas: Latent energetic impressions (see energetic impressions).

Vedas: Literally it means knowledge, but used here to mean the Book of Knowledge, the oldest book in the world. There are four Vedas.

yoga: Union; that which leads one back to the original Source; generally understood to mean a path or a practice leading to the divine. The different kinds or paths of yoga, starting with the body are, Hatha Yoga, Karma Yoga, Laya Yoga, Bhakti Yoga and Raja Yoga.

RECOMMENDED READING

BOOKS ON HEALING

These are the books that have been the most helpful to me out of the many that are available. I have listed the healing books *in order of importance*, the first being the most comprehensive or giving the greatest overview of the subject. Also, there are many different translations of some of these books. These are the specific translations that I have found to be the clearest and most complete.

Choa Kok Sui. *Pranic Healing*. York Beach, ME: Samuel Weiser Inc., 1990.

Yogi Ramacharaka. *The Science Of Psychic Healing*. Essex, England: L.N.Fowler, 1964.

———. *The Science Of Breath*. London: Society of Metaphysicians, 1986.

Frawley, David. *Ayurvedic Healing*. Salt Lake City, UT: Passage Press, 1989.

Lad, Vasant. *Ayurveda: The Science Of Self-Healing*. Twin Lakes, WI: Lotus Publications, 1984.

Ranade, Subhash. *Natural Healing Through Ayurveda*. Salt Lake City, UT: Passage Press, 1993.

Chopra, Deepak. *Quantum Healing: Exploring the Frontiers of Body, Mind, Medicine*. New York: Bantam, 1984.

OTHER VALUABLE RESOURCES

Brunton, Paul, ed. *Conscious Immortality: Conversations with Ramana Maharshi.* Tiruvannamalai, India: Sri Ramanasramam, 1984.

Frawley, David. *Gods, Sages and Kings.* Salk Lake City, UT: Passage Press, 1991.

———. *Tantric Yoga and the Wisdom Goddesses.* Salt Lake City, UT: Passage Press, 1994.

Godman, David, ed. *No Mind, I Am the Self.* Nellore District, A. P., India: Sri Lakshmana Ashram, 1988

———. *Papaji.* Boulder CO: Avadhuta Foundation, 1993

Kingsland, Kevin and Venika, trans. *Hathapradipika.* England: Grael Communications, 1977.

Sri Nisargadatta Maharaj. *Consciousness and the Absolute.* Jean Dunn, ed. Durham, NC: Acorn Press, 1994.

———. *I Am That.* Bombay, India: Chetana Ltd., 1991

———. *Prior to Consciousness.* Jean Dunn, ed. Durham, NC: Acorn Press, 1985.

———. *Seeds of Consciousness.* Jean Dunn, ed. Durham, NC: Acorn Press, 1990.

Sri Ramana Maharshi, *Be as You Are.* ed. David Godman. New Delhi: Penguin Books India, 1992.

Muni, Ganapathi. *Sri Ramana Gita.* Tiruvannamalai, India: Sri Ramanashramam, 1992.

Poonja, Sri H. W. L. *The Truth Is.* Huntington Beach, CA: Yudhishtara, 1995.

———. *Wake Up and Roar,* vols. I and II. Maui, Hawaii: Pacific Center Publications, 1992.

Bhagwan Shree Rajneesh, *Meditation: The Art of Ecstasy.* New York: Harper Collins, 1978.

Swami Ramanananda Saraswati, trans. *Advaita Bodha Deepika.* Tiruvannamalai, India: Sri Ramanashramam, 1990.

———., ed. *Talks with Sri Ramana Maharshi.* Tiruvannamalai, India: Sri Ramanashramam, 1984.

———., trans. *Tripura Rahasya.* Tiruvannamalai, India: Sri Ramanashramam, 1989.

Swami Venkatesanada, trans. *Yoga Vasistha: The Supreme Yoga.*

Swami Venkatesanada, trans. *Yoga Vasistha: The Supreme Yoga.* Shivanandanagar, Uttar Pradesh, India: Divine Life Society, 1991.

Woodroffe, John (Arthur Avalon). *The Serpent Power.* Madras, India: Ganesh & Co., 1989.

INDEX

Atreya came to pranic healing through his own search for healing. He has lived in India for six years studying meditation, pranic healing, and yogic psychology. In 1991 he met his teacher, who presented him to the ancient method of self-in-quiry. Originally from Southern California, Atreya lives in Paris, where he practices Ayurvedic and pranic healing. He is currently writing a second book about Ayurvedic medicine. Groups who want to arrange workshops or seminars are welcome to contact Atreya through the publisher.